Karl Jenkins

CANTATA MEMORIA

For the Children of Aberfan
Er mwyn y plant

for soprano & baritone soli,
young voices, chorus & orchestra

Libretto by Mererid Hopwood

VOCAL SCORE

Boosey & Hawkes Music Publishers Ltd
www.boosey.com

Published by Boosey & Hawkes Music Publishers Ltd
Aldwych House
71–91 Aldwych
London
WC2B 4HN

www.boosey.com

ISMN 979-0-060-13328-2
ISBN 978-1-78454-284-9

First impression 2017

Printed by Halstan:
Halstan UK, 2–10 Plantation Road, Amersham, Bucks, HP6 6HJ. United Kingdom
Halstan DE, Weißliliengasse 4, 55116 Mainz. Germany

Cover design: Deutsche Grammophon GmbH, Berlin, adapted by RF Deisgn UK Limited
Cover photo: © Mark Owen / Trevillion Images

Karl Jenkins photo: Rhys Frampton

Music origination by Jon Bunker

Commissioned by S4C to commemorate the 50th anniversary
of the Aberfan tragedy on 21st October 1966.

Comisiynwyd y gwaith gan S4C i goffáu hanner canmlwyddiant trychineb Aberfan ar Hydref yr 21ain 1966.

A sincere and humble acknowledgment is offered to the Trustees of the Aberfan Memorial Charity in giving their blessing to the creation of *Cantata Memoria*.

KJ

CONTENTS

CANTATA MEMORIA

For the children of Aberfan
Er mwyn y plant

PREFACE

Cantata Memoria commemorates the Aberfan tragedy of 21 October 1966. It was on this day that 116 children and 28 adults perished when a coal spoil tip enveloped Pantglas Junior School together with some houses in Aberfan, South Wales. Aged 22, I was in my first term at the Royal Academy of Music, London, at the time. Inevitably the disaster had a massive impact on me and millions of others.

Two years ago, I was approached by Ian Jones, CEO of S4C (Sianel Pedwar Cymru – Channel Four Wales), and Hefin Owen of Rondo Media and offered a commission to compose a work commemorating the 50th anniversary of the tragedy. Feeling privileged, humbled and honoured to have been chosen, I immediately accepted, whilst also being mindful of the responsibility the commission carried in writing something with integrity and accessibility that would connect and move *everyone* – the bereaved who are still with us, those who remember and those who come to this catastrophe anew. Paradoxically, dealing with a subject that lies so deep in the soul of the Welsh was both a harrowing and uplifting experience, but the journey was made easier and more rewarding by my travelling companion, Mererid Hopwood, the brilliant Welsh poet, academic and linguist who has written a remarkable libretto.

And while the work starts in Aberfan, alas we must be mindful of how it might encompass other heartbreaking tragedies involving children. Think of Dunblane (1996), the Beslan school siege (2004), the Korean ferry disaster and the Peshawar School massacre (both 2014) – each one a disaster too many. We have all been children, and many of us are parents and grandparents, and my hope is that *Cantata Memoria* is symbolic, concerning childhood and the cherishing of the precious young as well as offering a memorial in music for the disaster in Wales. As Mererid says, "we sincerely hope the work speaks from two hearts to many hearts".

This work is music and a poem. It is not a documentary, nor even a dramatisation, but it does include a conflation of ideas and facts that were relevant and by now part of the legacy. There wasn't just the one cortège, for example. Some events remain open to debate but we do know that *All Things Bright and Beautiful* was sung at Pantglas School from time to time and also *Myfanwy* (by Joseph Parry from nearby Merthyr Tydfil) on one occasion by soldiers who dug for victims. *Myfanwy* was also the first piece sung by the Ynysowen Male Choir, formed after the tragedy with the intention of raising money for charity while providing a social activity for the local men. It was said also that birdsong was not heard in the hours before or after the tragedy.

The text is multilingual, in English, Welsh and Latin (four texts from the Requiem Mass), while also incorporating various other languages for specific words (for example 'why' and 'light' are sung in Welsh, English, Swedish, Latin, Spanish, German, French, Dutch and Italian). It is hoped these many languages symbolise how the memorial is at once both specific and universal.

The work is in two distinct sections but performed continuously. The first (*c*20 minutes) deals with the tragedy and the immediate aftermath, and the second (*c*35 minutes) moves from darkness to light, reliving memories and celebrating childhood, ending with the Requiem's *Lux æterna* (everlasting light).

Cantata (from the Italian *cantare*, meaning 'to sing') has come to mean a work for soloist(s), choir and orchestra, and *memoria* is both Latin and Italian for memory or remembrance.

SYNOPSIS

It was raining on 21 October 1966 as the school day began (raindrops simulated in the orchestration by harp, percussion, then pizzicato strings *etc*). The first section opens as the adult choir sings:

(1) *Pitran, patran* (onomatopoeic Welsh for rain). This moves into *All Things Bright and Beautiful* sung by the children. A poignant line in the hymn has sinister ambiguity in our context as 'the river running by' alludes beyond the innocent song to the hidden river running underneath the village that contributed to the disaster. A recurring rumble, *twrw* (pronounced 'too-roo'), is hinted at in the orchestration, gradually morphing the mood from beauty and optimism into horror and darkness. The cataclysmic ending is followed by an unbearable pause of eeriness and disbelief before:

(2) *Then Silence* where the solo baritone intones: 'Nothing. In that black silence Not a sound.' A distant surreal refrain (as though sung by the lost children) of the well-known Welsh children's nursery rhyme *Heno, heno, Hen blant bach* (which returns as a motif throughout the work) precedes the return of the *pitran, patran* text with the 'pa' of *patran* morphing into the 'pa' of *paham* (Welsh for 'why'). The *a cappella*

singing of an adaptation of J S Bach's chorale *It is Enough* is then heard, with the word 'why?' sung in many languages. In this chorale (oft-quoted by composers, including Alban Berg in his Violin Concerto) we hear every note in the chromatic scale, in part chosen here to represent *all* humanity. This continues, without pause, into …

(3) *Cortège*. This begins with a short extract from the Welsh song *Myfanwy*, by Joseph Parry, which again begins with the word *paham* (why) but initially with darker harmonies than usual. It has become part of the Aberfan story that *Myfanwy* was sung by rescuers as they dug for victims. Here it is taken by a solo baritone, joined by by male voices and then a haunting euphonium, both redolent of the Welsh Valleys' musical tradition. The last refrain of the song becomes the motif, in the minor key, for the cortège itself. With much angst, the names of all the victims are intoned (the children by the adult choir, and the adults by the children) in tandem with the text of the *Benedictus* from the Latin Mass: 'Benedictus qui venit in nomine Domini' (Blessed is he who comes in the name of the Lord). The movement ends with the denunciation by a bereaved father at one of the inquests, 'buried alive by the National Coal Board' (which was, eventually, found culpable). This phrase echoes the rhythm of the Welsh we hear in the distance: 'bwrw glaw mân ac mae'r dagrau yn disgyn' (as the rain falls so too do the tears). To close the first section there follows:

(4) *Lament for the Valley* for solo violin and strings, with the choir intoning the text of the *Agnus Dei* (Lamb of God) as a background to the violin solo.

The second section deals with remembrances of happier times, a celebration of childhood and a metamorphosis towards 'light' from the 'darkness inside'. This transition is also reflected in the music that becomes lighter and begins with:

(5) *Lacrimosa Lullaby*, where the Latin mass text from the *Dies iræ* ('That day of tears and mourning … grant them eternal rest') works as a counterpoint to the words of the main song: '*Lacrimosa* dies illa, *Lacrimosa* sky, *Lacrimosa* crystal kisses, *Lacrimosa* lullaby … *Lacrimosa* silent feathers, *Lacrimosa* fly, *Lacrimosa* hush my baby, *Lacrimosa* lullaby'. It was said that no birdsong was heard before or after the disaster, and this idea and symbolism of a bird is heard in the next two movements.

(6) '*Did I hear a bird?* … Did I hear the flutter of wings, Like the sound of apron strings Unravelling? What have I heard? Just a little bird that keeps on falling, falling, from an empty thunder-cloud, sounding of loss – a loss so loud.' This poignant questioning leads to:

(7) *Satin Feathers*, a reworking of the traditional Welsh folksong *Aderyn Du*, in which we hear an exhortation to the bird to 'Bring the music to my valley … Bring the joy and bring the laughter, Bring them back to stay forever.' We are then suddenly back at school with:

(8) *And-a-half*, which opens with typical school-yard banter: 'I'm bigger than you – I'm seven years old', 'That's nothing – I'm seven and a half!' 'I'm stronger than you – I'm eight years old', 'That's nothing – I'm eight and a half!' 'If you're so pretty, give Johnny a kiss.' 'But Johnny is ugly. For shame! I'll tell Miss!' … before the characters of the parents take over with memories of their own childhood. The recollections continue in:

(9) '*And once upon a time* … When time was forever and tomorrow was never, In that once upon a time that was yours and mine …' Here the adults cherish each moment of each child's life, before stopping to ponder what happens:

(10) *When the shadow dies*. From dark despair this song reflects on questions that have no answers: 'How should we weep when the shadow dies?' In this searching it is the children themselves who offer the way forward towards the light: 'but if to be alive is to belong Then we must keep, Still, this song … Sing it, for our children loved light'.

We close with:

(11) *Lux æterna* (everlasting light), which begins with a musical quotation from my own *Requiem* before the word 'light' (as, previously, 'why') is sung in various languages. This moves into the children singing a school assembly hymn *If I were a Beautiful Twinkling Star* (reminiscent of *All Things Bright and Beautiful*) before continuing with 'light' in Latin, English and Welsh. The orchestra concludes the piece not in pomp and ceremony but rather with a glistening orchestration of celesta, glockenspiel and various bells to depict 'light', the word which, quietly spoken by the children and sung by the soprano, brings the piece to a close.

Karl Jenkins, May 2016

Cantata Memoria
For the children of Aberfan
Er mwyn y plant

1 – Pitran, patran

Chorus
Pitran, patran, (onomatopoeic Welsh for raindrops)*
Titrwm, tatrwm,
Dagrau agos, dagrau glaw, Near tears, tears of rain
Pitran, patran,
Titrwm, tatrwm,
Cysgu blantos bore ddaw. Hush, little children, morning will come again

Pitran, patran,
Titrwm, tatrwm,
Dagrau agos, dagrau glaw,
Pitran, patran,
Titrwm, tatrwm,
Cysgu blantos bore ddaw.

Young voices
All things bright and beautiful,[1]
All creatures great and small,
All things wise and wonderful:
The Lord God made them all.

The purple-headed mountain,
The river running by,
The sunset and the morning
That brightens up the sky.

All things bright and beautiful,
All creatures great and small,
All things wise and wonderful:
The Lord God made them all.

The tall trees in the greenwood,
The meadows where we play,
The rushes by the water,
To gather every day

All things bright and beautiful,
All creatures great and small,
All things wise and wonderful:
The Lord God made them all.

Chorus
Titrwm, tatrwm *etc*

Twrw, twrw *etc*

Twrw, bwrw *etc* bwrw: *hitting, throwing ('it's raining' in Welsh is literally 'it's hitting/throwing rain')*

Bore bwrw, bore bach *etc* bore bach: *first light (literally 'little morning')*

Soprano solo
Bach, bach.

2 – Then Silence
Tawelwch fu

Baritone solo
Nothing.
Dim. Nothing.
In that black silence
Yn y tywyllwch†
Not a sound.
Does dim sŵn.

Chorus
Dim, dim *etc* Nothing, nothing

Baritone solo
Nothing, not a sound *etc*
Does dim sŵn.

Young voices sing the hwiangerdd *(lullaby)*
Heno, heno, Tonight,
Hen blant bach, Little children,
Gwely, gwely, Bed,
Hen blant bach. Little children,
Dime, dime, dime, Halfpenny,
Hen blant bach, Little children.
Dime, dime, dime,
Hen blant bach.

Chorus
Pitran, patran *etc* (raindrops)

Baritone solo
Nothing, not a sound.
In that black silence
Nothing, not a sound.
Darkness inside and the dark keeps on growing.
Does dim sŵn.
Yn y tywyllwch
Does dim sŵn.
Dim ond tywyllwch, tywyllwch sy'n tyfu.
Paham? Why?

Chorus[2]
Lord, why, oh why?
Perché, perché, perché?
Pour quelle raison?
Warum, mein Gott?
Quare Domine mi?
¿Por qué, mi Señor?
Oh why, oh why?
Waroom?
Varför?
It is enough.
Paham? Paham?

3 – Cortège

Baritone solo
Why is it anger, O Myfanwy,[3]
That fills your eyes so dark and clear?
Your gentle cheeks, O sweet Myfanwy,
Why blush they not when I draw near?
Where is the smile that once so tender
Kindled my love so fond, so true?
Paham mae dicter, O Myfanwy,[3]
Yn llenwi'th lygaid duon di?
A'th ruddiau tirion, O Myfanwy,
Heb wrido wrth fy ngweled i?
Pa le mae'r wên oedd ar dy wefus
Fu'n cynau 'nghariad ffyddlon ffôl?

Chorus
Give me your hand, my sweet Myfanwy,
But one last time, to say "farewell".
Rho im dy law, Myfanwy dirion
I ddim ond dweud y gair "Ffarwel"

---

* Reference translations shown in sanserif type.
† Alternative Welsh text is italicised. Where the text is in Welsh only the score contains an English transliteration for non-Welsh speakers. See also pronunciation guide on page xii.

Chorus: child victims
Antony John Sullivan,
John Islwyn Jones,
Richard Phillip Goldsworthy,
Royston Barrett,
Timothy Grey,
Paul Jones,
Anthony David Hill,
Clive and Philip Mumford,
Marilyn Carol Howells,
Megan Robbins,
Robert Breeze,
Janette Lynne Brown,
Jean Launchbury,
Julie Jeannine Regan,
Suzanne Meredith,
Julie Pryce,

SATB simultaneously:
Soprano
David Davies,
Jeffrey Derek Needs,
Christine George,
Susan Jones,
Yvonne Drage,
Christine Prosser,
Gillian Irene Jones,
Terrence Davies,
Stephen Vaughan and Angela Hopkins.

Alto
Robert Garfield Jones,
Robert and Barbara Minney,
Royston Carl Davies,
David Trevor Davies,
Peter Williams,
Eryl Mai Jones,
June Margaret Williams,
Pamela Heaman,
Victoria Symonds.

Tenor
Wayne England,
Valmai Mary Owen,
Cheryl Mortimer,
Norma Mumford,
Martine Anne Short,
Michael Jones,
Annette Smith,
Karen O'Brien,
Jacqueline Powell,
Dennis Arscott,
Sandra Donovan.

Bass
Carol Williams,
Daphne Fudge,
Brian Davies,
Linda Hodkinson,
Howell Lloyd and Gareth Victor Evans,
Keith Williams,
Kevin Thomas Jones,
Michael Collins,
Robert Coffey.

Young voices
Benedictus qui venit in nomine Domini. Hosanna in excelsis.[4]

Blessed is he who comes in the name of the Lord. Hosanna in the highest.
Bendigedig yw'r hwn sy'n dyfod yn enw yr Arglwydd. Hosanna yn y goruchaf.

SATB simultaneously:
Soprano
Andrew Rees,
Raymond John and Peter Collins,
Susan Crotty,
Annette Hughes,
Sharon Lewis,
Anthony Joseph Watkins,
David William Williams,
Ann Catherine Lee,
Lynda and Carol Anderson,
Sandra Leyshon,
Marylyn and Carl Minett.

Alto
Desmond Carpenter,
Edwin Davies Evans,
John Anthony King,
Jennifer Haines,
Jean Winifred and Maureen Mary Evans,
Kay Bowns,
Carol Ann Carpenter,
Royston Hodkinson,
Pat and Tommy Probert,
Graham Williams,
Paul David Roberts,
Janet Jones,
Sylvia Richards,
Paul Davies.

Tenor
Joseph Wilkshire,
Roger Summers,
David Gareth Davies,
Howard David Prosser,
Dwynwen Griffiths,
Betty Edwina Bartlett,
Lorraine Isobel Richards,
Kelvin David and Malcolm Andrew,
Necia James,
Jill and Vincent Parfitt,
William Michael and Sheila Fitzpatrick.

Bass
Catherine Elizabeth Evans,
Avis Elizabeth Sullivan,
Gillian and Brian Michael Gough,
Randolph Tudor,
Robert Orville Jones,
Lyn Harding,
Merrill Barnard,
Ian Dougall,
Angela Williams,
Arthur O'Brien,
Corwyn T and Leighton Kerrie Reakes,
Dyfrig Hayes.

Chorus
Benedictus qui venit in nomine Domini. Hosanna in excelsis.

Young voices simultaneously: adult victims
Young voices 1
Richard Jones,
Lewis and Glenys Gabriel Jones,
Patricia Margaret Evans,
Gwyneth Collins,
Graham Edward and Sidney Russell,

William Henry Rees,
Frederick Richard Hansen,
Susannah Probert,
Marjorie Christine Evans.

Young voices 2
Evan George and Margaret Jane Carston,
John Morgan Edwards,
Brian Elvet Harris,
Nansi Williams,
Cassie Jones,[5]
Tydfil Jane Taylor,
Myrtle Irene and William Charles Thomas,
Evelyn Mary Jones,
Lucy May and Albert Gerald Mytton,
David Beynon,
Marjorie Ann Rees.

Young voices 3
Margaretta Bates,
Michael Davies,
Ann Jennings.

Chorus
Benedictus.
Buried alive by the National Coal Board.
Bwrw glaw mân ac mae'r dagrau yn disgyn.
As the rain falls so too do the tears.

Baritone solo
Bwrw glaw mân ac mae'r dagrau yn disgyn.
Buried alive by the National Coal Board.

4 – Lament for the Valley
Marwnad y Cwm
Agnus Dei

Young voices & chorus
Agnus Dei, qui tollis peccata mundi, miserere nobis, qui tollis peccata mundi, dona nobis pacem.

Lamb of God, who takes away the sins of the world, have mercy on us, who takes away the sins of the world, grant us peace.
Oen Duw, sy'n tynnu ymaith bechodau'r byd: trugarha wrthym, dyro inni dy dangnefedd.

5 – Lacrimosa Lullaby[6]
Lacrimosa 'Maban Glân

Baritone solo
Lacrimosa dies illa,
Lacrimosa sky,
Lacrimosa crystal kisses,
Lacrimosa lullaby.

That day of tears and mourning
(lacrimosa*: tearful*)

Lacrimosa secret rivers,
Lacrimosa sigh,
Lacrimosa raindrops quiver,
Lacrimosa lullaby.

Lacrimosa dies illa,
Lacrimosa 'nghân,
Lacrimosa cusan grisial,
Lacrimosa 'maban glân.

Y dydd hwnnw o ddagrau a galar
(*lacrimosa*: dagreuol)

Lacrimosa'r afon ddyfnaf,
Lacrimosa'r cwm,
Lacrimosa dagrau'n crynu,
Lacrimosa 'ngalar trwm.

Young voices
Lacrimosa dies illa,
Qua resurget ex favilla
Judicandus homo reus:
Huic ergo parce Deus.

That day of tears and mourning, when from the ashes shall arise all humanity to be judged, spare us by your mercy, Lord.
Y dydd hwnnw o ddagrau a galar, pan gyfyd o'r llwch yr holl fyd i farnedigaeth, gwared ni drwy dy drugaredd, O Arglwydd.

Baritone solo
Pie Jesu Domine,

Gentle Lord Jesus,
Iesu'r Arglwydd Tirion,

Baritone solo & young voices
dona eis requiem.

grant them eternal rest.
rhodded iddynt dragwyddol hedd.

All voices
Lacrimosa lullaby.
Lacrimosa 'maban glân.

Baritone solo
Lacrimosa silver arrows,
Lacrimosa cry,
Lacrimosa hurt my heartbeat,
Lacrimosa lullaby.

Lacrimosa silent feathers,
Lacrimosa fly,
Lacrimosa hush my baby,
Lacrimosa lullaby.

Lacrimosa'n saethau arian,
Lacrimosa'n gri,
Lacrimosa'n guriad calon,
Lacrimosa 'nghalon i.

Lacrimosa'r bluen ddistaw,
Lacrimosa dos,
Lacrimosa hysh fy mhlentyn,
Lacrimosa cysga'r nos.

Chorus
Lacrimosa dies illa,
Qua resurget ex favilla
Judicandus homo reus:
Huic ergo parce Deus.

Young voices
Pie Jesu Domine,

Baritone solo & chorus

dona eis requiem.

Baritone solo & young voices
Lacrimosa lullaby.
Lacrimosa 'maban glân.

6 – Did I hear a bird?

Young voices
Did I hear a bird?
Not a word.
Did I hear a song?
Perhaps long ago.
(But I don't think so.)
Did I hear the flutter of wings,
Like the sound of apron strings
Unravelling?
What have I heard?
Just a little bird

Baritone solo
That keeps on falling, falling
From an empty thunder-cloud,
Sounding of loss –
a loss so loud.

Chorus

Heno, heno,	*Tonight,*
Hen blant bach,	*Little children,*
Gwely, gewly,	*Bed,*
Hen blant bach,	*Little children,*
Dime, dime,	*Halfpenny,*
Hen blant bach,	*Little children.*
Dime dime,	
Hen blant bach.	

Young voices & baritone solo
Can you hear a bird?
Just a word?
Can you hear a song?
'Twas long ago,
But I don't think so.

Can you hear the flutter of wings,
Like the sound of apron strings?
Hear a beating, beating wing?
Beating my heart,
Just a little bird
That keeps on calling, calling,
Calling softly from the crowd,
That keeps on calling, calling,
Calling for light,
A light so loud.

Chorus

Fory, fory,	*Tomorrow,*
Hen blant bach,	*Little children,*
Gwely, gwely,	*Bed,*
Hen blant bach,	*Little children,*
Dime, dime dime,	*Halfpenny,*
Hen blant bach.	*Little children.*

7 – Satin Feathers
Aderyn Du

Soprano solo
Little bird with satin feathers,
Take my tears across the waters,
Take my prayer and take my sorrow,
Take my heart until tomorrow.

Aderyn du a'i blufyn sidan,
A'i big aur a'i dafod arian,
Ei di drosta'i ar don yr heli
I holi hynt yr un 'rwy'n garu?

Baritone solo
Then bring the spring and bring the summer,
Bring the stars a little closer,
Bring the sun and make it golden,
Bring the daisies to my garden.

Aderyn du, a ddoi di eto,
Dod i'r ardd i chwarae cuddio,
Dod â'r blodau nôl i dyfu,
Dod â'r heulwen aur i wenu?

Soprano & baritone soli
Bring the music to my valley,
Bring it back again, and hurry,
Bring the joy and bring the laughter,
Bring them back to stay forever.

Aderyn du, a ga'i dy ffeindio
Yn y cwm yn canu eto?
Tyrd â'r miwsig, tyrd â'r chware,
Tyrd â'r plant yn ddiogel adre.

One, two, three things, I can't imagine
That my bird with wings of satin
Takes the night, the moon, the shadow,
And brings my children home tomorrow.

Un, dou, tri pheth sy'n anodd imi,
Cyfri'r sêr pan fo hi'n rhewi,
Pwyso sofrens aur yr eithin,
A deall i ble'r aeth y chwerthin.

Young voices & chorus
Bring the music to my valley,
Bring it back again, and hurry,
Bring the joy and bring the laughter,
Bring them back to stay forever.

Aderyn du, a ga'i dy ffeindio
Yn y cwm yn canu eto?
Tyrd â'r miwsig, tyrd â'r chware,
Tyrd â'r plant yn ddiogel adre.

All voices
Forever.
Nôl adre.

8 – And-a-half
Blwyddyn-a-mis

Young voices
I'm bigger than you – I'm seven years old.
That's nothing – I'm seven and a half!

Dwi'n fwy na thi, dwi'n saith mlwydd oed.
'Mond hynny? – Dwi'n saith mlwydd a mis!

I'm stronger than you – I'm eight years old.
That's nothing – I'm eight and a half!

Dwi'n gryfach na thi – dwi'n wyth mlwydd oed.
'Mond hynny? – Dwi'n wyth mlwydd a mis!

I'm prettier than you – I'm nine years old.
That's nothing – I'm nine and a half!

Dwi'n bertach, lot, na thi – dwi'n naw mlwydd oed.
'Mond hynny? – Dwi'n naw blwydd a mis!

I'm cleverer than you – I'm ten and a quarter.
That's nothing – I'm ten and a half!

Dwi'n ddoethach, lot, na thi – dwi'n ddeg, bron, a hanner.
'Mond hynny? – Wel dwi'n un deg un!

If you're so big, tell Billy he's slow.
I can't today, I've got a bad toe.

A thi mor fawr, dwed wrth Jac: ti'n slo'!
Alla'i ddim nawr, na'i 'neud rywbryd 'to.

If you're so strong, go on lift this stone!
I can't today, I've got a bad … bone.

A thi mor gryf, coda'r garreg hon!
Alla'i ddim nawr, mewn crys newydd sbon.

He can't today, he's got a bad … bone.

All e ddim nawr, mewn crys newydd sbon.

If you're so pretty, give Johnny a kiss.
But Johnny is ugly. For shame, I'll tell Miss!

A thi mor brydferth, rho gusan i Ben.
Ond mae Beni'n rhy salw! Dwi'n dweud wrth Miss Gwen!

If you're so clever, what's three hundred million divided by nine over two?
That's easy peasy lemon squeezy … but I'm not telling you!

A thi mor glyfar, beth yw tair miliwn pum cant wedi rhannu gyda thri?
Mae hynny'n haws na chaws na phawsi … ond so fi'n gweud 'tho ti!

Chorus
And somewhere between the years-and-a-half,
When the sky would skip and the sun would laugh,
When the yard was the sea and the wall was the land,
When the whole wide world could fit in a hand,
We sang, we played, we sought, we found,
We teased, we joked, we gathered around,
We wrote, we read, we built, we drew,
Before the years-and-a-half all flew
Away.

A rhywle'n y bwlch rhwng blwyddyn a mis,
A'r haul yn rhoi'i aur heb holi am bris,
Ar yr iard roedd y môr, a'r hen wal fach pen draw
Ydoedd ffin y byd mawr a phawb law yn llaw,
Pob awr yn ŵyl, pob gêm yn hwyl,
Pob llais yn gân, pob gair yn lân,
Pob lliw yn llun, pob gwg yn wên,
Cyn hedfan y misoedd oll yn un
Am byth.

9 – And once upon a time
Unwaith amser maith yn ôl

Soprano & baritone soli
And once upon a time,
When time was mine,
Before you and I
Knew how to fly,
Before the minute without meaning,
Before the end of each beginning,
Once upon a time,

Ac amser maith yn ôl,
A thi yn fy nghôl,
Cyn dyfod y glaw,
Cyn gollwng dy law,
A chyn yr eiliad heb ddim golau,
A chyn y diwedd i bob dechrau,
Amser maith yn ôl,

Chorus
Once upon a time that was yours and mine.
Amser maith yn ôl, d'amser di a mi.

(the above repeated)

Chorus & young voices
And once upon a time,
When time was together,
When the worlds were nearer
And the skies were clearer,
Once upon a time,
When time was forever and tomorrow never,
In that once upon a time that was yours and mine,
Yours and mine.

Ac amser maith yn ôl,
Dyddiau dau yn dynnach,
Pob dim yn agosach,
Aer uwchben yn lasach,
Amser maith yn ôl,
Dyddiau dau'n fyth bythoedd ac yfory'n oesoedd,
Yn ein hamser maith yn ôl, d'amser di a mi,
Dim ond ni.

Soprano & baritone soli
yours and mine.
di a mi.

10 – When the shadow dies

Soprano & baritone soli
How should we weep when the shadow dies,
Fading, slipping till the sun lies
Asleep?

Should we now leave,
For the stars shed no light?

Or shall we mourn by the shallow moon
That has no dawn,
No day, say,
Shall we stay?

And still,
Shall we grieve by the shallow grave
Of a flown-away life like a fallen leaf,
And if so, how?

And when winter blows,
Might we rest by the empty tree?
Shall we try? Should I?
Nobody knows.

But if to be alive is to belong
Then we must
Keep
Still
This song.

Chorus, young voices & optional soprano & baritone soli
Sing it until the end of the night,
Canwn
Sing it, sing it, for our children loved light,
Canwn, canwn

Soprano & baritone soli
my child loved light.

11 – Lux æterna[7]

Young voices, then soprano & baritone soli, then chorus
Lux æterna luceat eis, Domine: cum sanctis tuis in æternum, quia pius es. Requiem æternam dona eis, Domine, et lux perpetua luceat eis, quia pius es.

Let everlasting light shine upon them, O Lord, with your saints for ever, for you are merciful. Eternal rest grant them, O Lord, and let perpetual light shine upon them, for you are merciful.
Llewyrched arnynt oleuni gwastadol, gyda dy saint am byth, oherwydd rwyt ti'n drugragog. Dyro iddynt orffwys tragwyddol, O Arglwydd, a llewyrched goleuni tragwyddol arnynt, oherwydd trugarog wyt ti.

Young voices & soprano & baritone soli
'Light' *in various languages*

Young voices
If I were a beautiful twinkling star[8]
I'd shine on the darkest night,
I'd seek where the dreariest pathways are
And light them with all my might.

Though sun and moon I cannot be
To make the whole world bright,
I'd find some little cheerless spot
And shine with all my might.

Pe bawn i yn seren fach loyw lân[8]
Yn gwenu ar fron y nos,
Mi fynnwn oleuo'r holl gonglau du
A'r ffordd sydd yn mynd i'r rhos.

Er nad wyf i na haul na lloer
I'r cread mawr i gyd,
Gall plentyn bychan lawenhau
Un cornel bach o'r byd.

Young voices, chorus altos
Lux æterna luceat eis, Domine: cum sanctis tuis in æternum, quia pius es.

Chorus

Sêr y Goleuni,	*Star of light,*
Seren dân,	*Star of fire,*
Goleuni,	*Light,*
Seren gân.	*Star of song.*

Young voices
Lux æterna luceat eis, Domine:

Soprano & baritone soli
cum sanctis tuis in æternum, quia pius es.

Young voices & chorus sopranos & altos
'Light' *in various languages*

Soprano solo & young voices
light.
glân.

[1] Words by Cecil Frances Alexander (1818–95). Melody by William Henry Monk (1823–89).
[2] Adaptation of the chorale 'Es ist genug' ('It is enough'): melody by Johann Rudolf Ahle (1625–73), harmonised by J S Bach (1685–1750).
[3] 'Myfanwy': Welsh words by 'Mynyddog' (Richard Davies, 1833–77); English words anon. Melody by Joseph Parry (1841–1903).
[4] Latin text from the Mass.
[5] Catherine (Cassie) Jones.
[6] Latin text from the *Dies iræ* (13th century).
[7] Latin text from the Requiem Mass.
[8] English words by 'Grace Gleam' (Mrs L M Beal Bateman, 1843–after 1920) and F A Jackson (1867–1942); Welsh words by William Nantlais Williams (1874–1959). Melody by 'Nora C E Byrne' (Carey Bonner, 1859–1938).

PRONUNCIATION GUIDE

Welsh pronunciation for English speakers approximately as follows:

bach	'ch' as in Scottish 'loch'
cysgu	'kusgee', with 'us' as in 'cusp'
ddaw	'thou'
glaw	rhymes with 'ddaw'
dime	'dim-eh'
heno	'heh-no', with 'o' as in 'not'
pa-ham	'pah-ham', with 'a' as in 'apple'

Cantata Memoria was first performed on 8 October 2016 at the Wales Millennium Centre, Cardiff, by Elin Manahan Thomas (soprano), Bryn Terfel (bass-baritone), Joo Yeon Sir (violin), Catrin Finch (harp), David Childs (euphonium), Jody Jenkins (percussion)

Cywair (chorus master: Islwyn Evans
CF1 (chorus master: Eilir Owen Griffiths)
Côr Caerdydd chorus master: Gwawr Owen
and the young voices of Côr Heol y March (chorus master: Eleri Roberts) and
Côr y Cwm (chorus master: Elin Llywelyn-Williams, co-director: Gavin Ashcroft)

Sinfonia Cymru (leader: Benjamin Baker)

Conducted by Sir Karl Jenkins.

Recording available on DG 0289 479 6486, by the above performers.

SCORING

Soprano Solo
Baritone Solo

Chorus of Young Voices

SATB chorus

Solo Violin (see notes)
Solo Euphonium (optional)

Descant Recorders (optional)
Piccolo
2 Flutes
2 Oboes
Cor anglais
2 Clarinets in B♭
Bass Clarinet
2 Bassoons
Contrabassoon
4 Horns in F
3 Trumpets in B♭
2 Tenor Trombones
Bass Trombone
Tuba

Timpani
Percussion (5)★
Celesta
Organ or Keyboard (optional)
Harp
Strings

★glockenspiel, xylophone, vibraphone, tubular bells, bell tree, triangle, finger cymbals, tambourine, tenor drum, 2 bass drums (large),†
cymbals, suspended cymbal, tam-tam (large)

†1st Bass Drum may be substituted by Taiko Drum

NOTES

1. The Solo Violin part may be played either by a soloist or by the leader/concertmaster. To allow for all eventualities there are parts for Solo Violin, for Violin I including Solo, and for Violin I excluding Solo.
2. The Solo Euphonium part may be played instead by Horn 1 or principal Cello and is cued into these parts. To allow for all eventualities there are parts for Cello including Solo and for Cello excluding Solo. The Euphonium part is supplied at concert pitch (bass clef) and in B♭ (treble clef).
3. Descant Recorders (a minimum of two) are optionally scored, in movement 6 only, and it is suggested that this part be played by members of the Young Voices. A separate recorder part is included in the set; for convenience the recorder part is also written into the Young Voices' score.
4. In the final movement all resting players play an assortment of triangles, bells and finger cymbals.

Duration: 50 minutes

Young voices' score on sale
Performance materials on hire

CANTATA MEMORIA

For the children of Aberfan

Er mwyn y plant

MERERID HOPWOOD
(b 1964)

KARL JENKINS
(b 1944)

1 – Pitran, patran

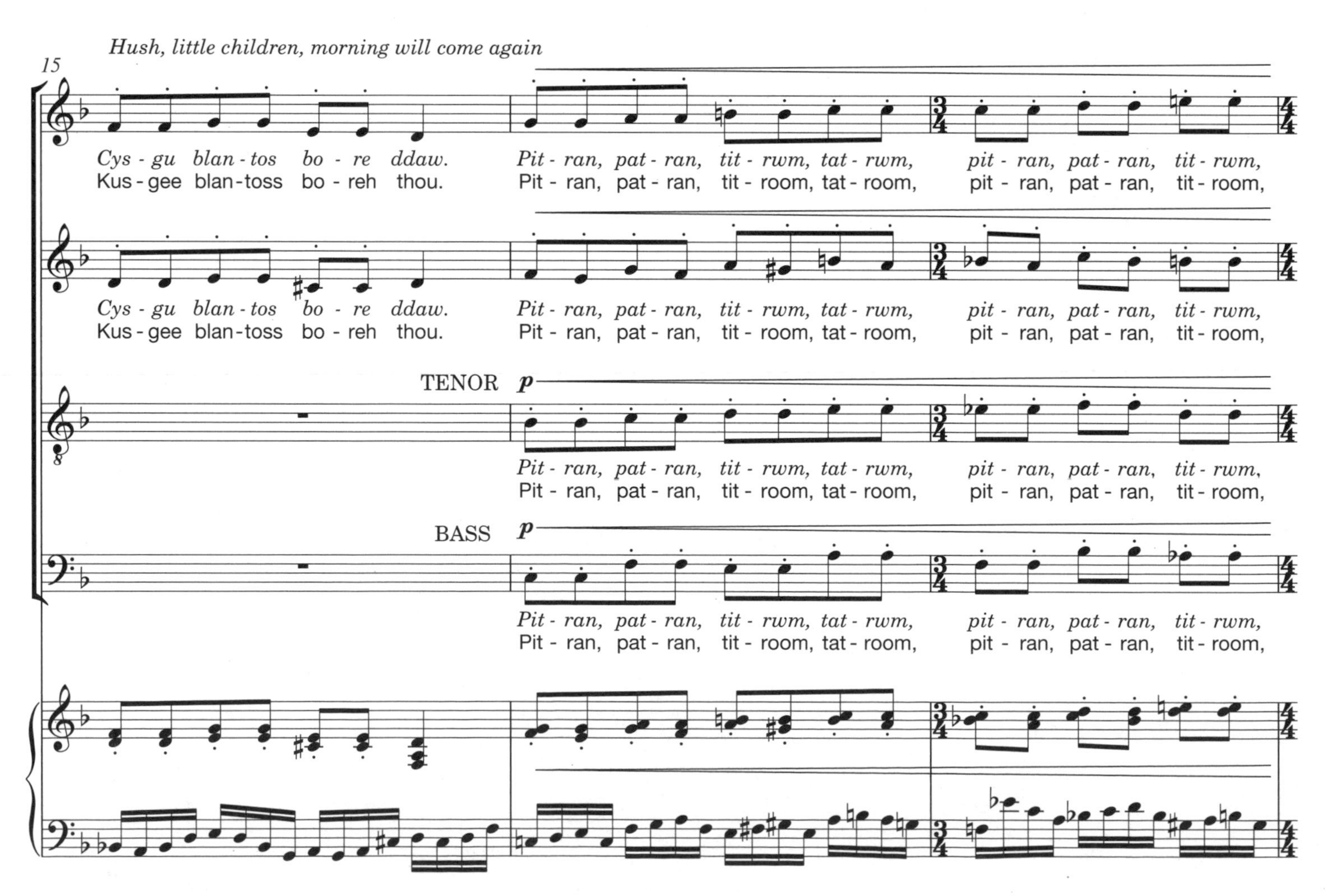

★English translation for reference purposes only – not for performance.

† rhymes with *ddaw*/'thou'

18
mp
pi-pi-pi-pi-pi.
p
Near tears, tears of rain
Pit - ran, pat - ran, tit - rwm, tat - rwm, Dag rau a - gos, dag rau glaw.
Pit - ran, pat - ran, tit - room, tat - room, Dag rye ah goss, dag-rye glou.
pi, pi-pi-pi-pi-pi.
pi, pi-pi-pi-pi-pi.
pi, pi-pi-pi-pi - pi.
sim
21
Hush, little children, morning will come again
pi-pi-pi-pi pa-pa-pa-pa ti - ti ti-ti ta-ta-ta-ta Cys - gu blan - tos bo - re ddaw.
Kus-gee blan-toss bo-reh thou.
2 YOUNG VOICES
div in 2
24
All things bright and beau - ti-ful, All crea-tures great and small, All things wise and won - der-ful: The
sim

27
Lord God made them all. The pur-ple-head - ed moun - tain, The ri - ver run - ning by, The
Lord God made them all. The pur-ple-head - ed moun - tain, The ri - ver run - ning by, The
sempre staccato
30
sun - set and the morn - ing That bright - ens up the sky. All things bright and beau - ti - ful, All
sun - set and the morn - ing That bright - ens up the sky. All things bright and beau - ti - ful, All
33
crea - tures great and small, All things wise and won - der - ful: The Lord God made them
crea - tures great and small, All things wise and won - der - ful: The Lord God made them
36
all. The tall trees in the green - wood, The
all. The tall trees in the green - wood, The
p
mp
p

39
mea-dows where we play, The rush - es by_ the wa - ter, To gath - er eve - ry day.
mea-dows where we play, The rush - es by_ the wa - ter, To gath - er eve - ry day.
sempre staccato

42
All things bright and beau - ti- ful, All crea-tures great and small, All things wise and won - der- ful: The
All things bright and beau - ti- ful, All crea-tures great and small, All things wise and won - der- ful: The

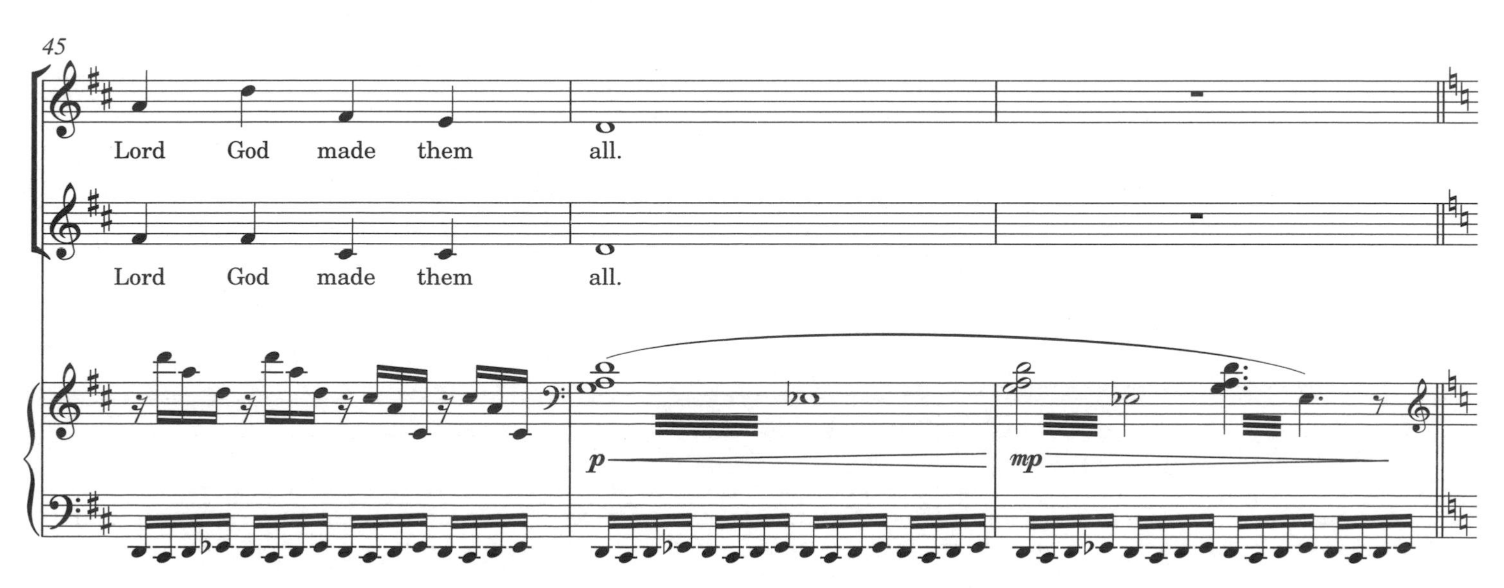
45
Lord God made them all.
Lord God made them all.
p
mp

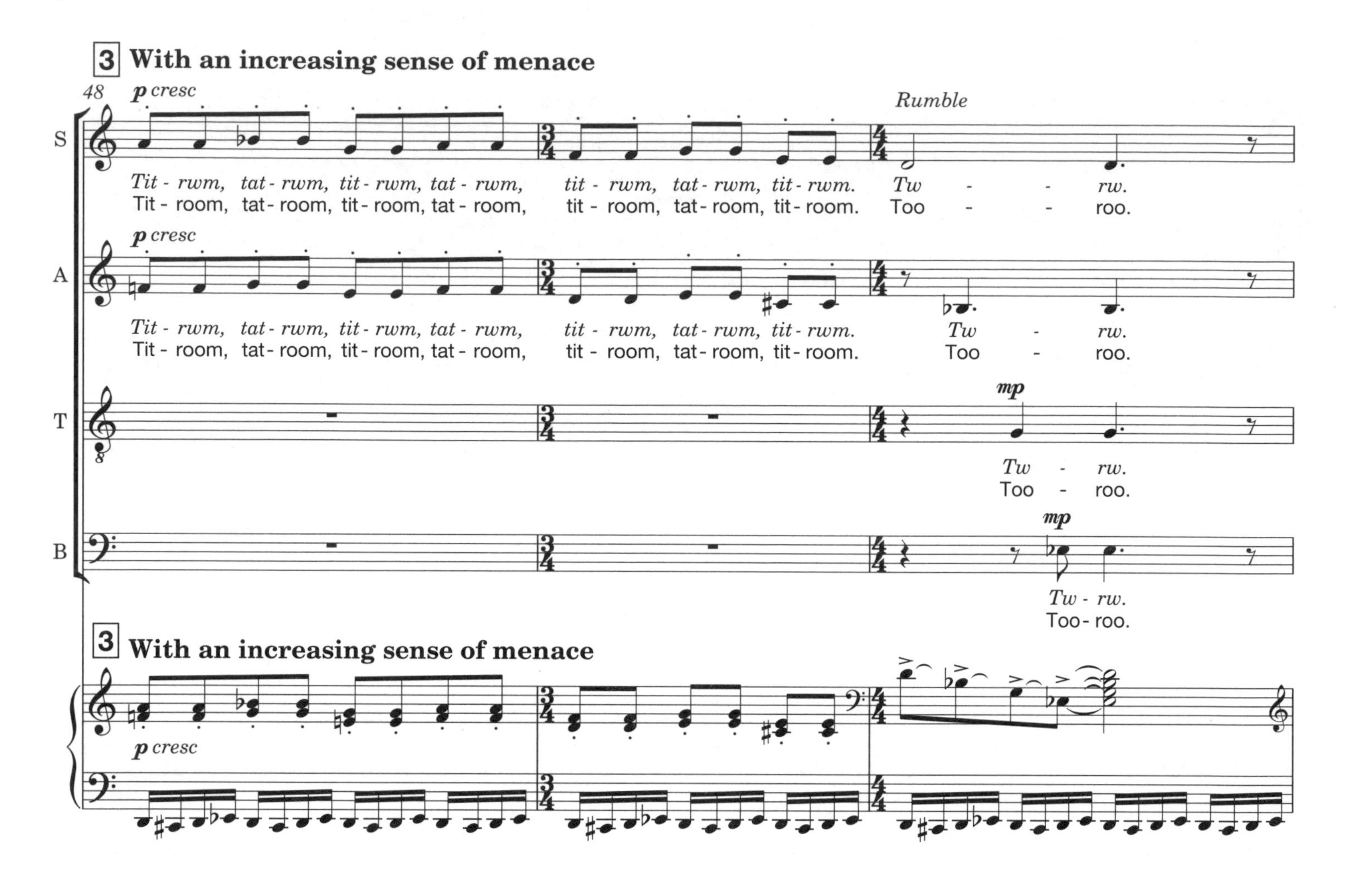
3 With an increasing sense of menace
48
p cresc
Rumble
S
Tit - rwm, tat - rwm, tit - rwm, tat - rwm, tit - rwm, tat - rwm, tit - rwm. Tw - - rw.
Tit - room, tat - room, tit - room, tat - room, tit - room, tat - room, tit - room. Too - - roo.
A
p cresc
Tit - rwm, tat - rwm, tit - rwm, tat - rwm, tit - rwm, tat - rwm, tit - rwm. Tw - rw.
Tit - room, tat - room, tit - room, tat - room, tit - room, tat - room, tit - room. Too - roo.
T
mp
Tw - rw.
Too - roo.
B
mp
Tw - rw.
Too - roo.
3 With an increasing sense of menace
p cresc

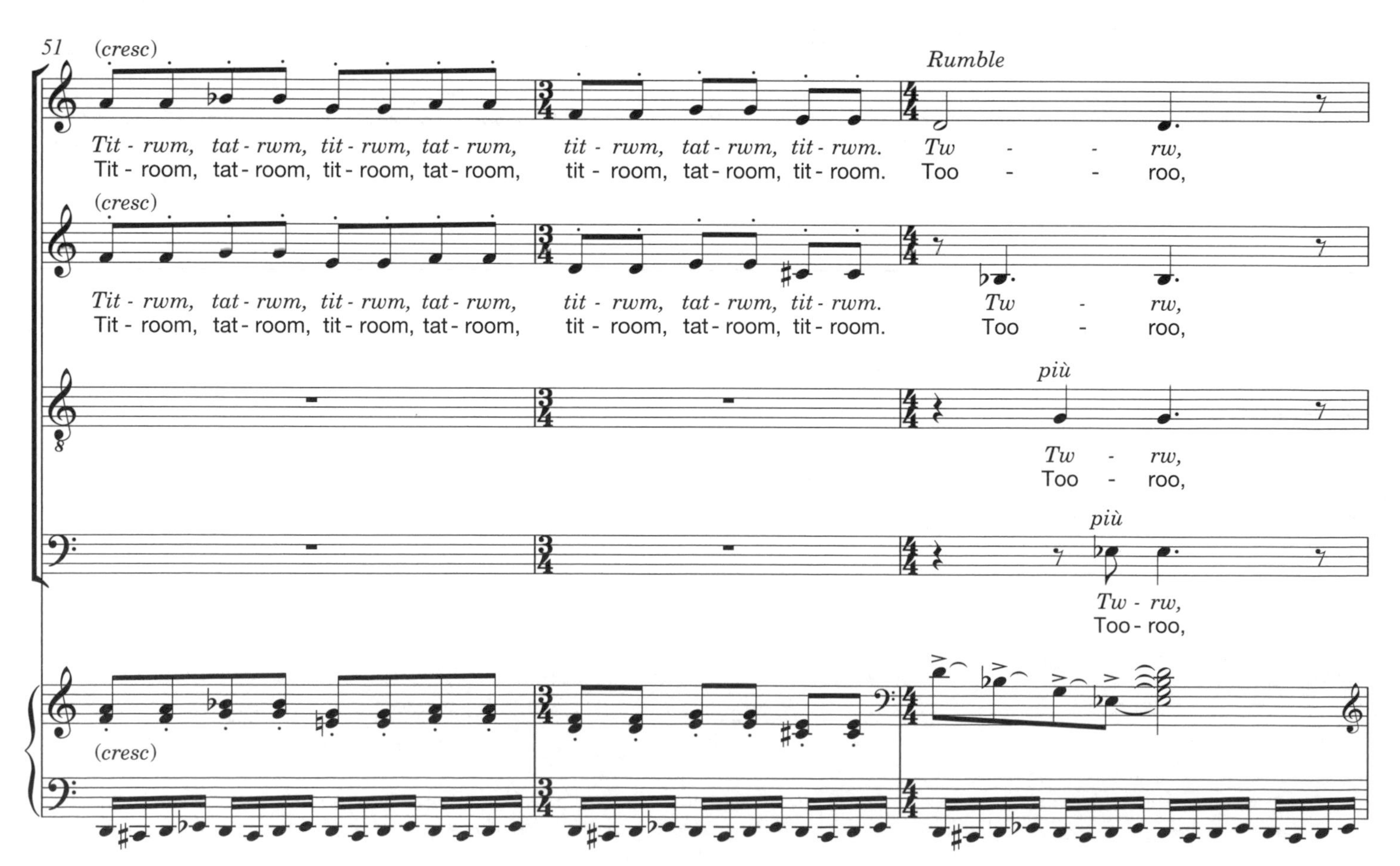
51 (cresc)
Rumble
Tit - rwm, tat - rwm, tit - rwm, tat - rwm, tit - rwm, tat - rwm, tit - rwm. Tw - - rw,
Tit - room, tat - room, tit - room, tat - room, tit - room, tat - room, tit - room. Too - - roo,
(cresc)
Tit - rwm, tat - rwm, tit - rwm, tat - rwm, tit - rwm, tat - rwm, tit - rwm. Tw - rw,
Tit - room, tat - room, tit - room, tat - room, tit - room, tat - room, tit - room. Too - roo,
più
Tw - rw,
Too - roo,
più
Tw - rw,
Too - roo,
(cresc)

54
Women div in 3
mp cresc
tw - rw, tw - rw, tw - rw, tw - rw, tw - rw,
too - roo, too - roo, too - roo, too - roo, too - roo,
Men div in 3
mp cresc
sim
8

57
(cresc)
4
unis
tw - rw, tw - rw, tw - rw, tw - rw, tw - rw, tw - rw,
too - roo, too - roo, too - roo, too - roo, too - roo, too - roo,
sempre

60
(cresc)
tw - rw, tw - rw, tw - rw, tw - rw, tw - rw, tw - rw, bw - rw, tw - rw,
too - roo, too - roo, too - roo, too - roo, too - roo, too - roo, boo - roo, too - roo,
(cresc)
tw - rw, tw - rw, tw - rw, tw - rw, tw - rw, tw - rw, bw - rw, tw - rw,
too - roo, too - roo, too - roo, too - roo, too - roo, too - roo, boo - roo, too - roo,
(cresc)
tw - rw, tw - rw, tw - rw, tw - rw, tw - rw, tw - rw, bw - rw, tw - rw,
too - roo, too - roo, too - roo, too - roo, too - roo, too - roo, boo - roo, too - roo,
(cresc)
tw - rw, tw - rw, tw - rw, tw - rw, tw - rw, tw - rw, bw - rw, tw - rw,
too - roo, too - roo, too - roo, too - roo, too - roo, too - roo, boo - roo, too - roo,
(cresc)

63
(cresc)
tw - rw, tw - rw, tw - rw, tw - rw, tw - rw, tw - rw, tw - rw, tw - rw,
too - roo, too - roo, too - roo, too - roo, too - roo, too - roo, too - roo, too - roo,
(cresc)
tw - rw, tw - rw, tw - rw, tw - rw, tw - rw, tw - rw, tw - rw, tw - rw,
too - roo, too - roo, too roo, too roo, too roo, too roo, too - roo, too - roo,
(cresc)
lw - rw, lw - rw, lw - rw, lw - rw, tw - rw, tw - rw, tw - rw, tw - rw,
too - roo, too - roo, too - roo, too - roo, too - roo, too - roo, too - roo, too - roo,
(cresc)
tw - rw, tw - rw, tw - rw, tw - rw, tw - rw, tw - rw, tw - rw, tw - rw,
too - roo, too - roo, too - roo, too - roo, too - roo, too - roo, too - roo, too - roo,
(cresc)

66
(cresc)
tw - rw, bw - rw, tw - rw, tw - rw, bw - rw, tw - rw, bw - rw, tw - rw, bw - rw,
too - roo, boo - roo, too - roo, too - roo, boo - roo, too - rooo, boo - roo, too - roo, boo - roo
68
hitting
morning
bw - rw. Bo - re, bo - re, bo - re bw - rw.
boo - roo. Bo - reh, bo - reh, bo - reh boo - roo.

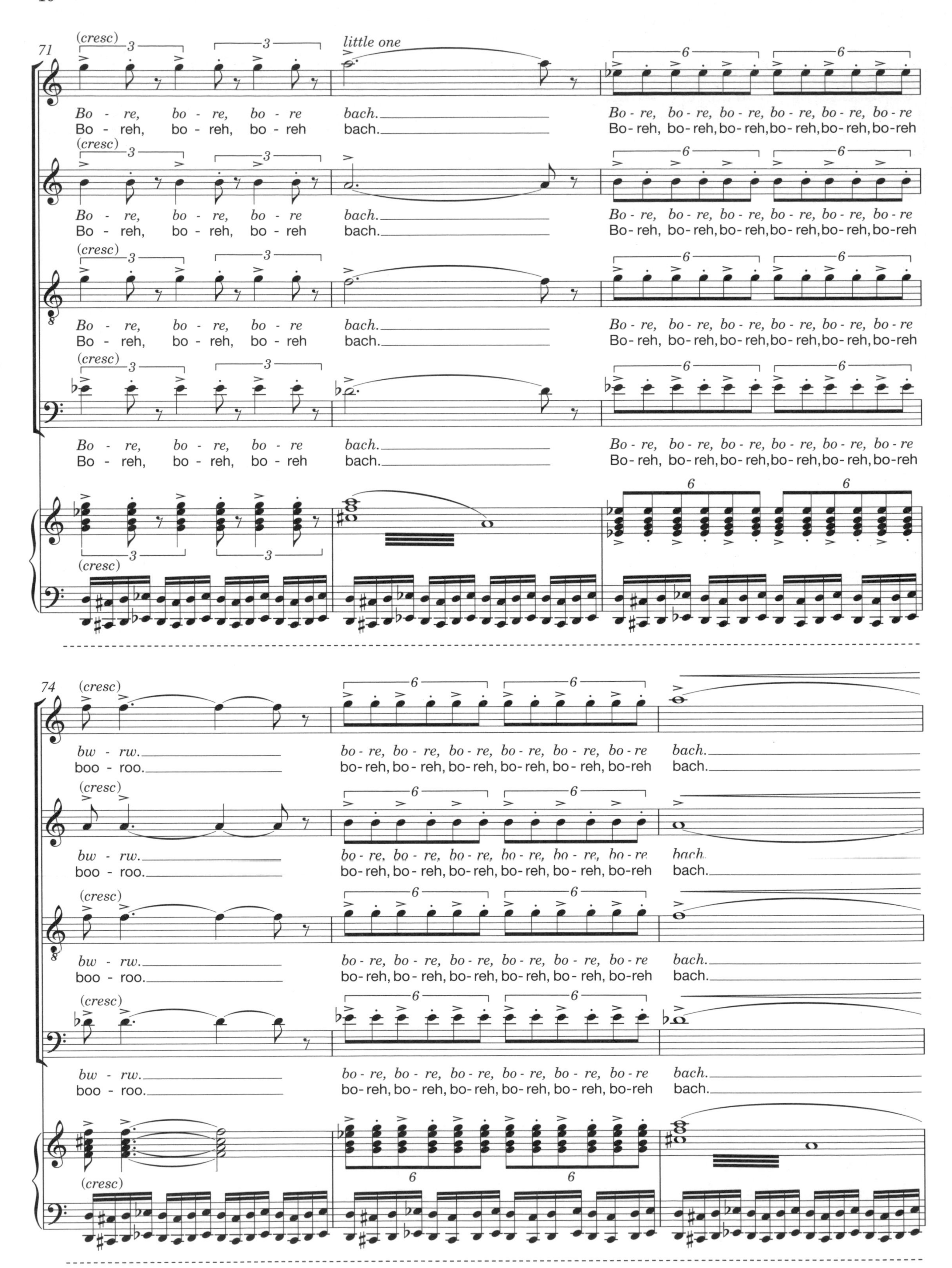
71
(cresc)
little one
Bo - re, bo - re, bo - re bach. Bo - re, bo - re, bo - re, bo - re, bo - re, bo - re
Bo - reh, bo - reh, bo - reh bach. Bo- reh, bo- reh, bo- reh, bo- reh, bo- reh, bo- reh
74
bw - rw. bo - re, bo - re, bo - re, bo - re, bo - re, bo - re bach.
boo - roo. bo- reh, bo - reh, bo- reh, bo- reh, bo- reh, bo- reh bach.

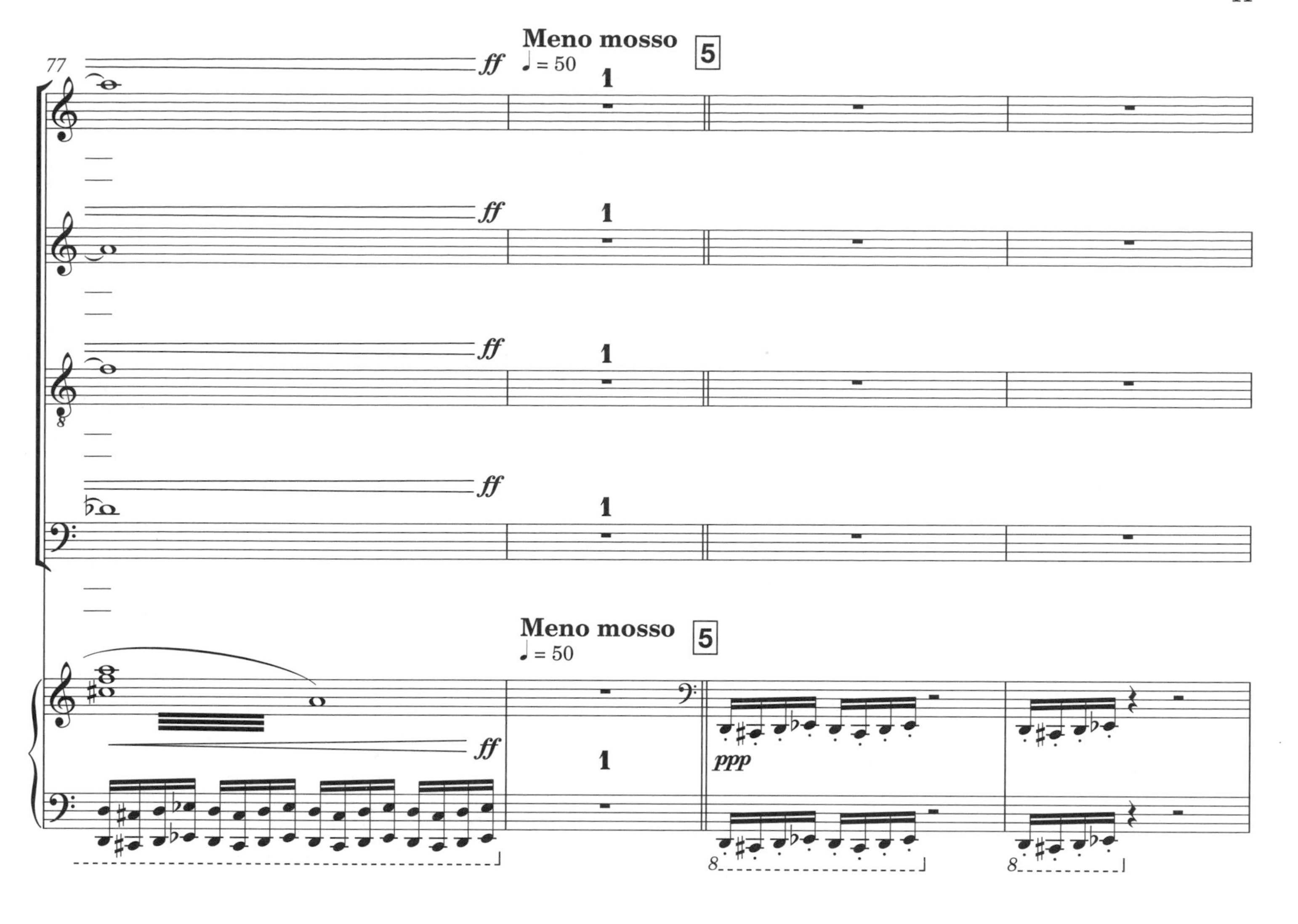
Meno mosso
♩ = 50
5
ff
ff
ff
ff
1
1
1
1
Meno mosso
♩ = 50
5
ff
1
ppp

molto rall
Largo
SOPRANO SOLO
pp
Bach,
bach.
ff
pp
1
1

2 – Then Silence

Tawelwch fu

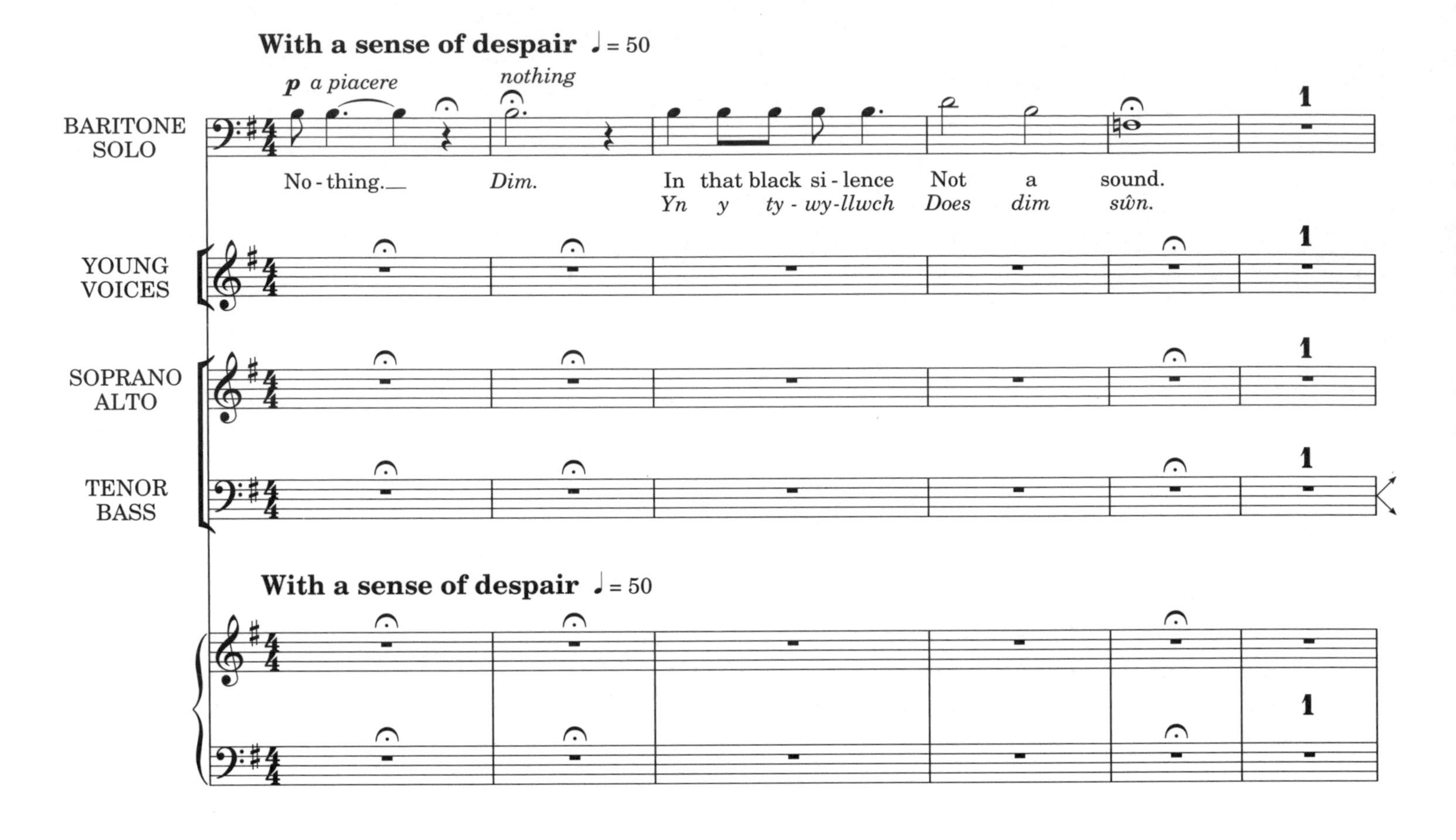

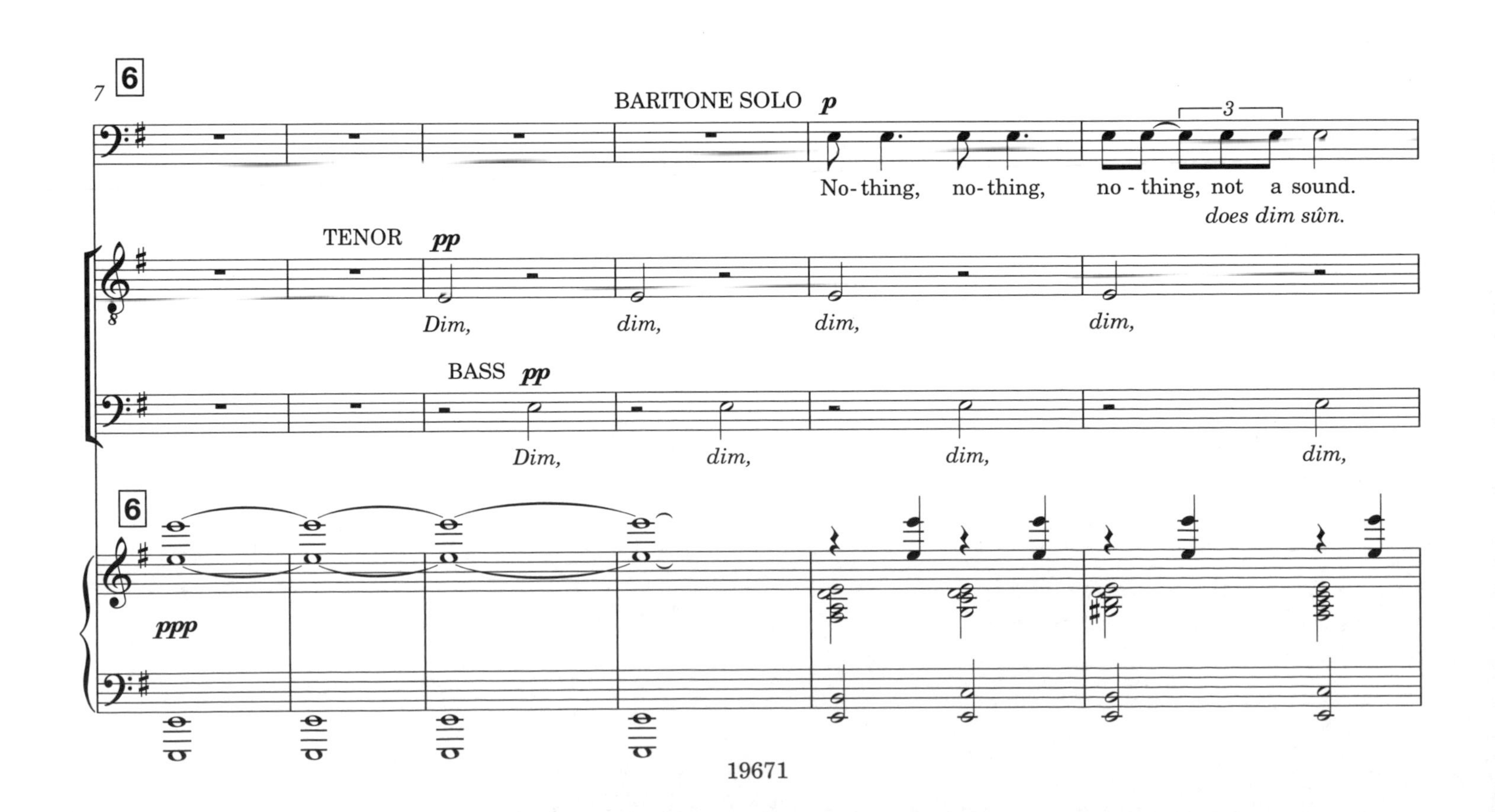

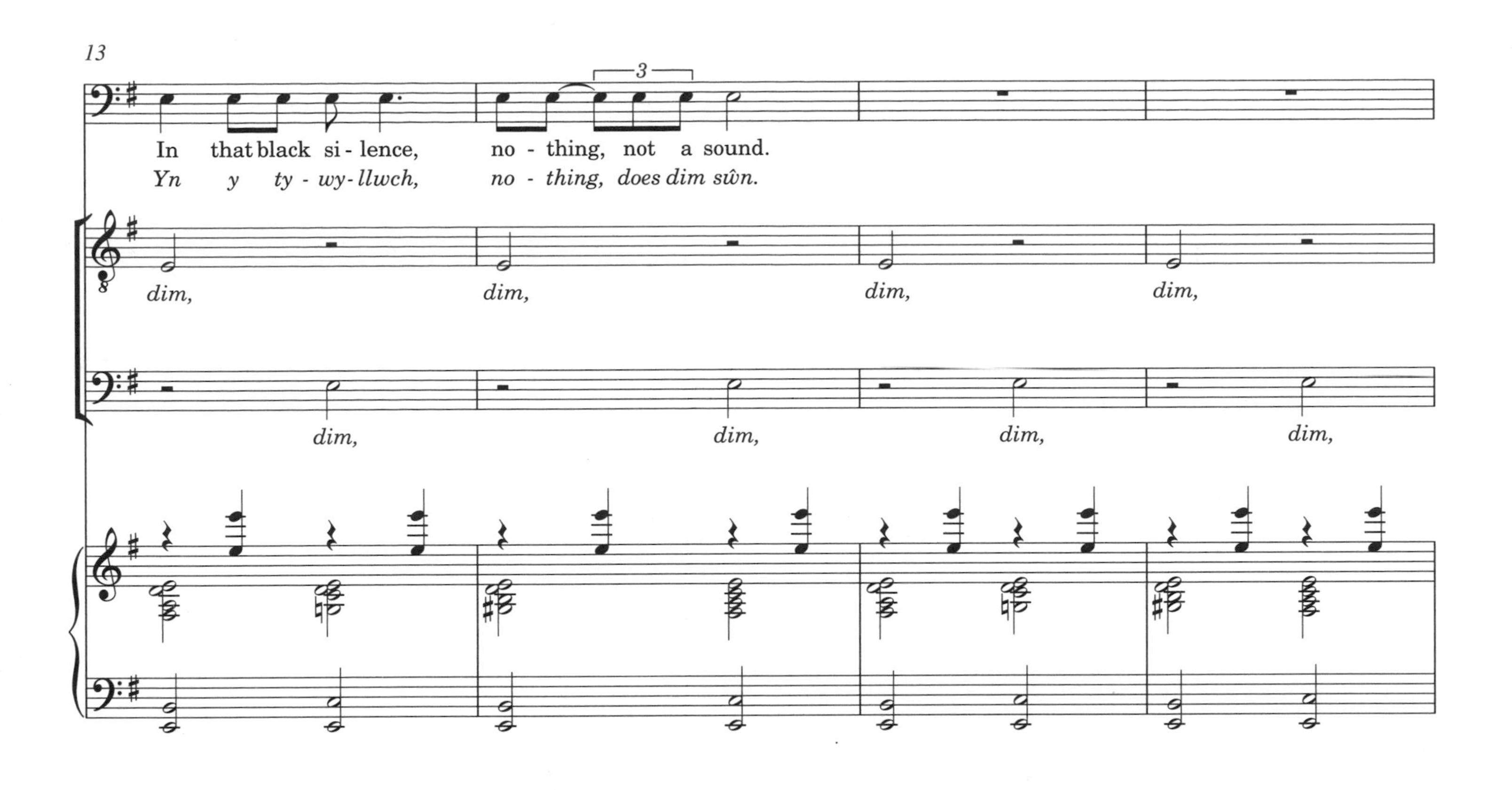
13
In that black si - lence,
no - thing, not a sound.
Yn y ty - wy - llwch,
no - thing, does dim sŵn.
dim, dim, dim, dim,
dim, dim, dim, dim,

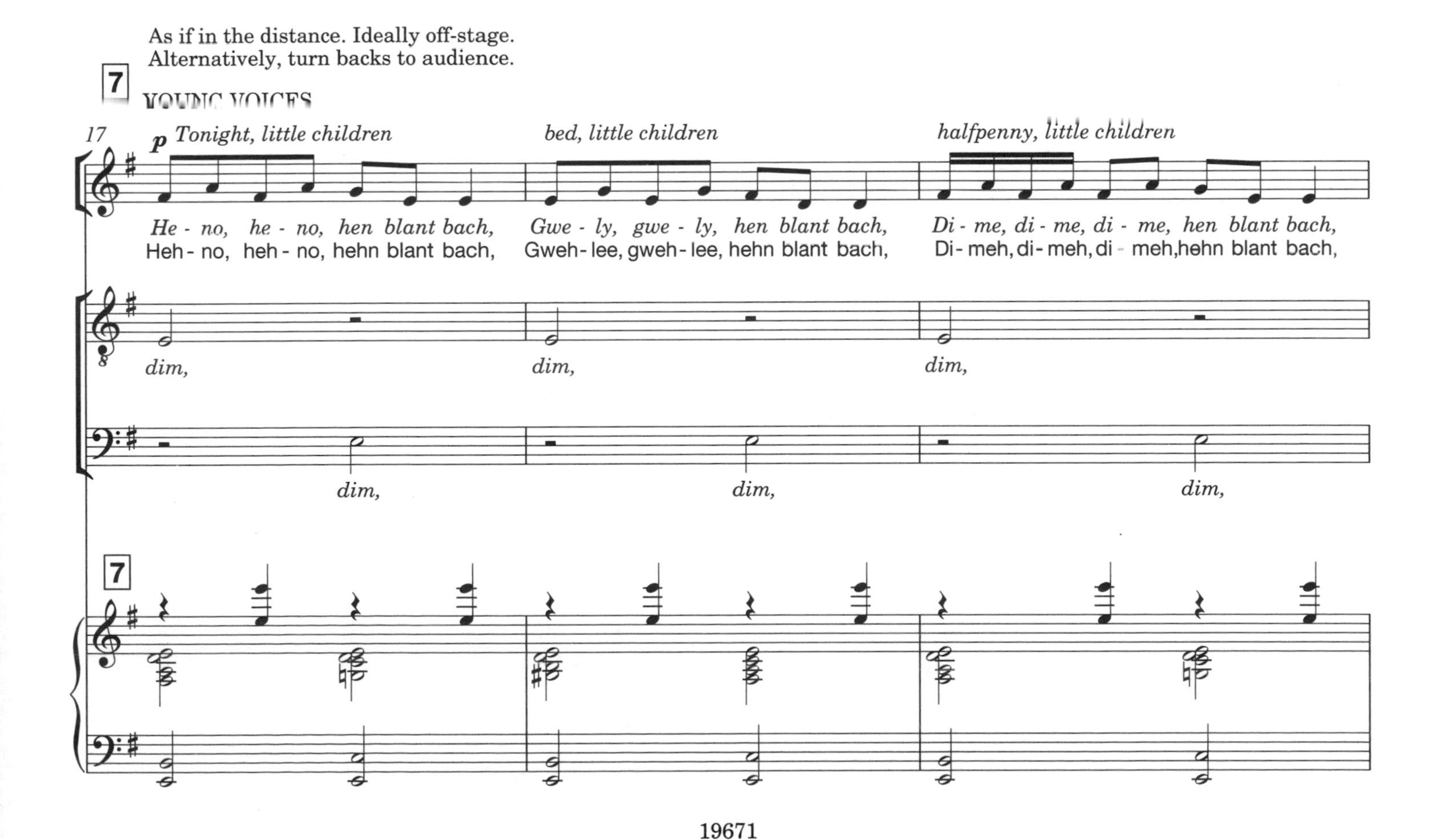
As if in the distance. Ideally off-stage.
Alternatively, turn backs to audience.
7
17
p
Tonight, little children
bed, little children
halfpenny, little children
He - no, he - no, hen blant bach,
Gwe - ly, gwe - ly, hen blant bach,
Di - me, di - me, di - me, hen blant bach,
Heh - no, heh - no, hehn blant bach,
Gweh - lee, gweh - lee, hehn blant bach,
Di - meh, di - meh, di - meh, hehn blant bach,
dim, dim, dim,
dim, dim, dim,
7

20
Di - me, di - me, di - me, hen blant bach.
Di- meh, di- meh, di- meh, hehn blant bach.
SOPRANO pp
Pit - ran, pat - ran.
Pit - ran, pat - ran.
ALTO pp
Pit - ran, pat - ran.
Pit - ran, pat - ran.
dim,
dim,
dim,
dim,
dim,
dim,

23 BARITONE SOLO
No- thing, no- thing, no - thing, not a sound. In that black si - lence
does dim sŵn. Yn y ty - wy - llwch,
Pit - ran, pat ran.
Pit- ran, pat - ran.
Pi-pi - pi - pi - pit - ran.
Pit - ran, pat ran.
Pit- ran, pat ran.
Pa-pa-pa-pa-pat ran.
dim,
dim,
dim,
dim,
dim,
dim,

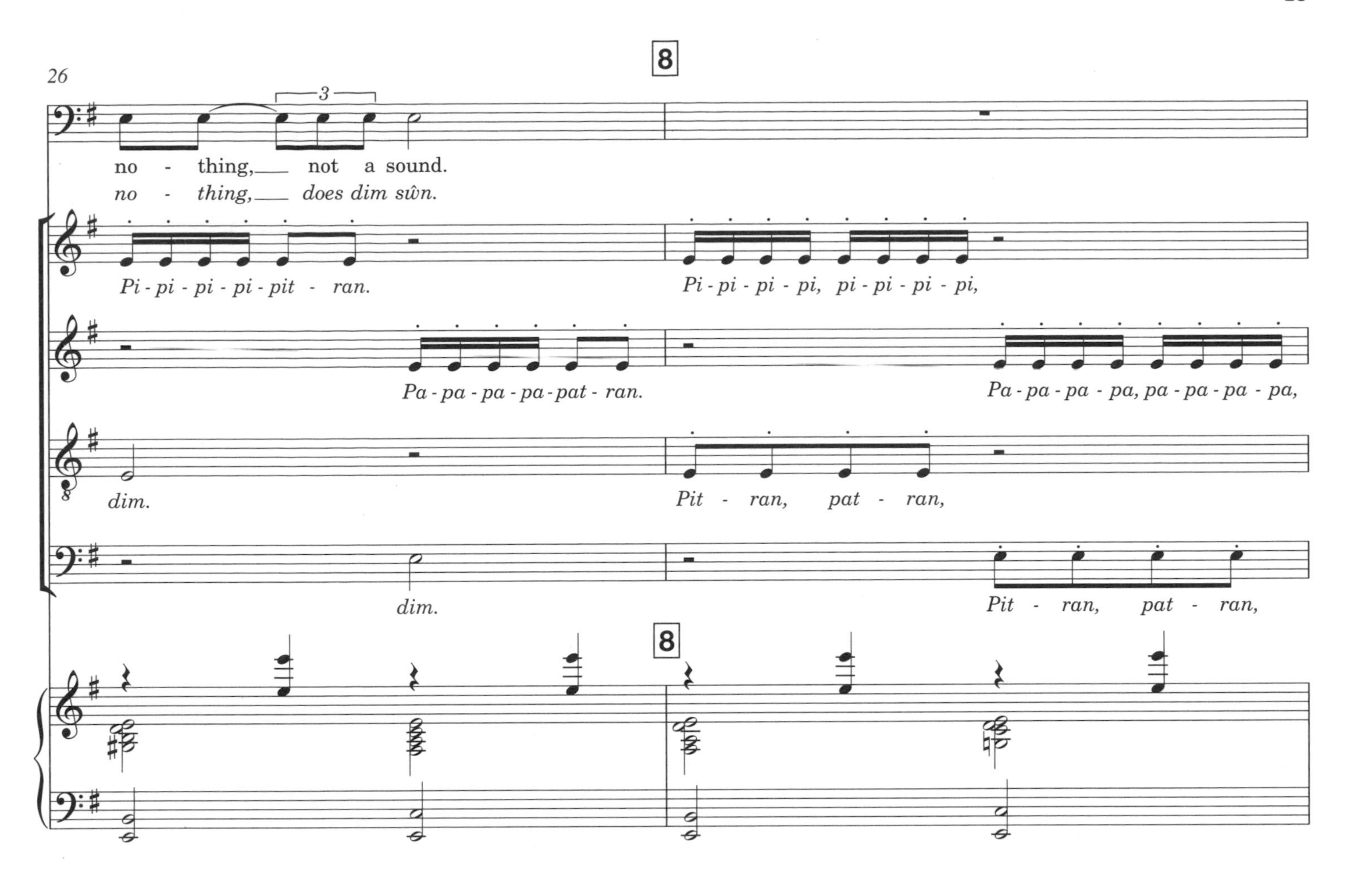
26
8
no - thing, not a sound.
no - thing, does dim sŵn.
Pi - pi - pi - pi - pit - ran.
Pi - pi - pi - pi, pi - pi - pi - pi,
Pa - pa - pa - pa - pat - ran.
Pa - pa - pa - pa, pa - pa - pa - pa,
dim.
Pit - ran, pat - ran,
dim.
Pit - ran, pat - ran,
8

28
Dark - ness in - side and the dark keeps on grow - ing.
Dim ond ty - wy - llwch sy'n ty - fu.
pi - pi - pi - pi, pi - pi - pi - pi.
Pa pa pa pa
Pa - pa - pa - pa, pa - pa - pa - pa - ham ham ham ham
pit - ran, pat - ran.
Pi - pi - pi - pi, pi - pi - pi - pi,
pit - ran, pat - ran.
Pa - pa - pa - pa, pa - pa - pa - pa,

30
Why?
Pa-ham, pa-ham, pa-
Pa-ham,
pa pa pa pa Pa-ham, pa-ham,
ham ham ham ham Pa-ham, pa-ham,
pi-pi-pi-pi, pi-pi-pi-pi, pi-pi-pi-pi, pi-pi-pi-pi,
pa-pa-pa-pa, pa-pa-pa-pa, pa-pa-pa-pa, pa-pa-pa-pa,
32
-ham, pa-ham, Pa-ham, pa-ham, pa-ham, pa-ham, pa-ham, pa-ham, pa-
pa-ham, pa-ham, pa - ham, pa-
pa-ham, pa-ham, pa - ham, pa-
pi pi-pi-pi, pi pi-pi-pi. Pa - ham, pa-
pa-pa-pa-pa, pa-pa-pa Pa - ham, pa-

35
-ham, pa-ham, pa-ham, pa-ham, pa-ham, pa-ham, pa-ham, pa-ham, pa-ham?
-ham. pa - ham?
-ham. pa - ham?
-ham. pa - ham?
-ham. pa - ham?

Più mosso
9
Adaptation of the chorale 'It is enough' by J S Bach
a cappella
40
p
mf
Italian
mp
French
Lord, why, oh why? Per - ché, per - ché, per - ché? Pour
Lord, oh why? Per - ché, per - ché, per - ché? Pour
Lord, why, oh why? Per - ché, per - ché, per - ché? Pour
Lord, why, oh why? Per - ché, per - ché, per - ché? Pour
Più mosso
9

45
German
Latin
poco f
pp
mf
quelle rai - son? Wa - rum, mein Gott? Qua - re,
quelle rai - son? Wa - rum, mein Gott? Qua - - re,
quelle rai - son? Wa - rum, mein Gott? Qua - - re,
quelle rai - son? Wa - rum, mein Gott? Qua - re,

49
Spanish
mp
f
Do - mi - ne mi? ¿Por qué, mi Se - ñor? Oh why, oh
Do - mi - ne mi? ¿Por qué, mi Se - ñor? Oh why, oh
Do - mi - ne mi? ¿Por qué, mi Se - ñor? Oh why, oh
Do - mi - ne mi? ¿Por qué, mi Se - ñor? Oh why, oh

53
Dutch
Swedish
why, why, why? Waa - rom, waa - rom? Var -
why, why, why? Waa - rom, waa - rom? Var -
why, why, why? Waa - rom, waa - rom? Var -
why, why, why? Waa - rom, waa - rom? Var -

rall
attacca
57
mf mp p pp
- - för? It is e - nough. Pa - ham, pa - ham?
- - för? It is e - nough. Pa - ham, pa - ham?
- - för? It is e - nough. Pa - ham, pa - ham?
- - för? It is e - nough. Pa - ham, pa - ham?
rall

3 – Cortège

With angst ♩ = 54
'Myfanwy'
mp
BARITONE SOLO
YOUNG VOICES
SOPRANO ALTO
TENOR BASS
Why
Pa -
With angst ♩ = 54
p
ff

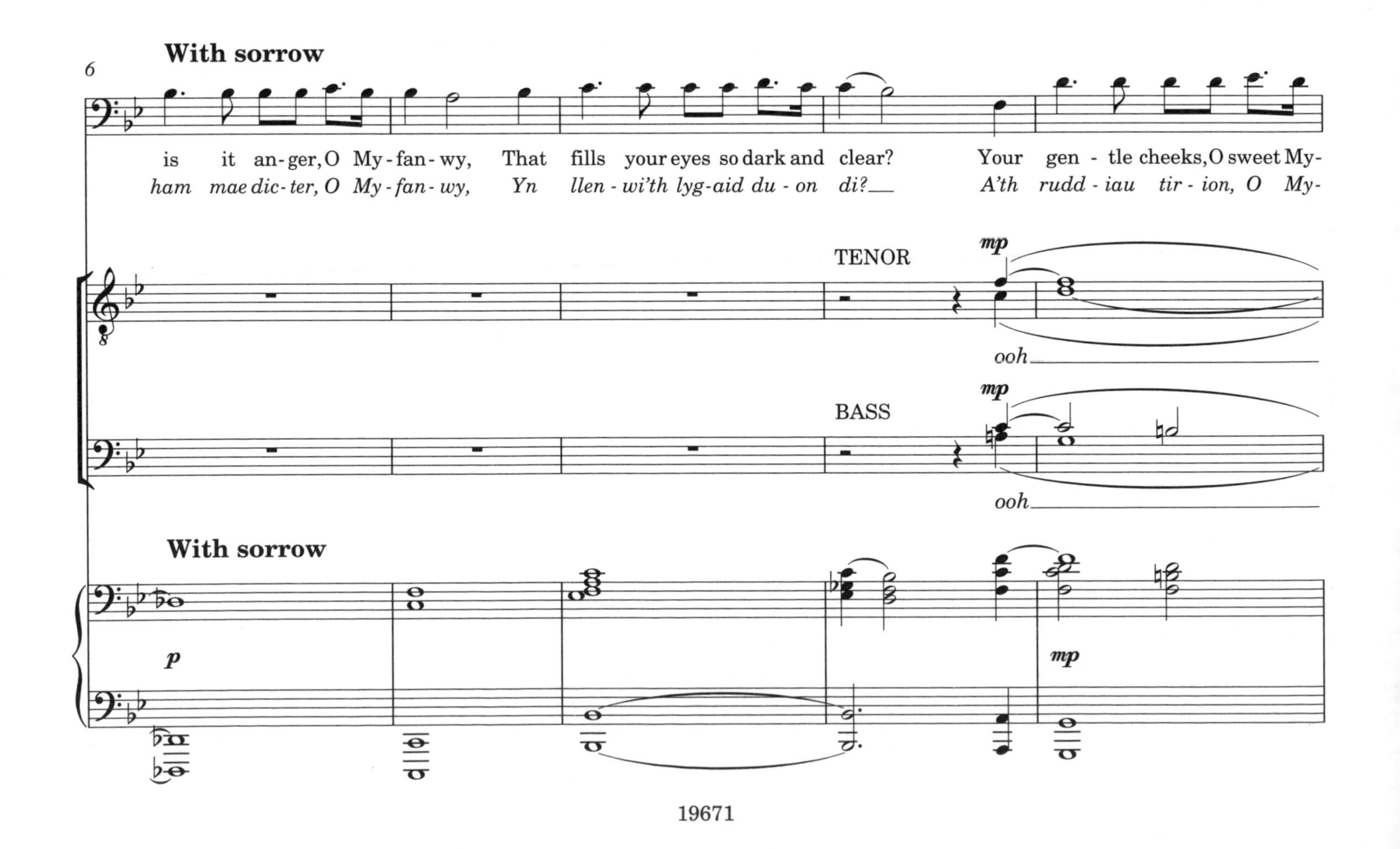
With sorrow
is it an-ger, O My-fan-wy, That fills your eyes so dark and clear? Your gen - tle cheeks, O sweet My-
ham mae dic-ter, O My-fan-wy, Yn llen-wi'th lyg-aid du - on di? A'th rudd-iau tir - ion, O My-
TENOR
mp
ooh
BASS
mp
ooh
With sorrow
p
mp

11
- fan- wy, Why blush they not when I draw near? Where is the smile that once so ten - der
- fan- wy, Heb wri - do wrth fy ngwe-led i? Pa le mae'r wên oedd ar dy we - fus Fu'n
ooh
ooh
10
16
Kin - dled my love so fond, so true? Give me your hand, my sweet My - fan- wy, But
cyn - nau'ngh ar-iad ffydd-lon ffôl? Rho im dy law, My - fan - wy dir-ion I
SOPRANO
Give me your hand, my sweet My - fan- wy, But
Rho im dy law, My - fan - wy dir-ion I
ALTO
Give me your hand, my sweet My - fan- wy, But
Rho im dy law, My fan - wy dir-ion I
TENOR
Give me your hand, my sweet My - fan- wy, But
Rho im dy law, My - fan - wy dir-ion I
BASS
Give me your hand, my sweet My - fan- wy, But
Rho im dy law, My - fan - wy dir-ion I
10
19671

20
one last time to say "fare-well".
ddim ond dweud y gair "Ffar-wel".
one last time to say "fare-well".
ddim ond dweud y gair "Ffar-wel".
one last time to say "fare-well".
ddim ond dweud y gair "Ffar-wel".
one last time to say "fare-well".
ddim ond dweud y gair "Ffar-wel".
one last time to say "fare-well".
ddim ond dweud y gair "Ffar-wel".
26
Meno mosso ♩ = 48
With angst
31
SOPRANO
Child victims
An-to-ny John Sul-li-van,
ALTO
John Is-lwyn Jones,

35
Rich-ard Phil-lip Golds-wor-thy,
Paul Jones, An-tho-ny Da-vid
Roy-ston Bar-rett, Tim-o-thy Grey,
38
Hill,
Ma-ri-lyn Ca-rol Ho-wells,
Ro-bert Breeze,
Clive and Phil-ip Mum-ford,
Me-gan Rob-bins, Ja-
11
41
Jean Launch-bu-ry,
Su-zanne Me-re-dith,
- nette Lynne Brown,
Ju-lie Jean-nine Re - gan,
Ju-lie Pryce,
11
sim

44
Da - vid Da- vies, Jeff-rey De-rek Needs, Chris-tine George, Su - san Jones, Y -
Ro-bert Gar-field Jones, Ro - bert and Bar-ba-ra Min-ney, Roy-ston Carl Da - vies,
TENOR mf
Wayne Eng-land, Val-mai Ma-ry O - wen, Che-ryl Mor-ti-mer, Nor - ma Mum - ford, Mar-
BASS mf
Ca - rol Wil-liams, Daph - ne Fudge, Bri - an Da - vies, Lin - da Hod-kin-son,

46
-vonne Drage, Chris - tine Pros - ser, Gil-lian I-rene Jones, Ter - rence Da-vies,
Da-vid Tre-vor Da-vies, Pe - ter Wil-liams, E-ryl Mai Jones, June Mar-g'ret Wil-liams,
-tine Anne Short, Mi-chael Jones, An-nette Smith, Ka-ren O' - Bri - en, Jac-que-line Po-well,
Ho - well Lloyd and Ga-reth Vic-tor E - vans, Keith Wil-liams, Ke-vin Tho-mas Jones,

48
12
Blessed
Bendigedig
f
YOUNG VOICES
div in 2
Be - ne - dic - tus, be - ne - dic - tus
f
Be - ne - dic - tus, be - ne - dic - tus
f
optional reinforcement for young voices
Ste - phen Vaughan and An-ge-la Hop - kins. Be - ne - dic - tus, be - ne - dic - tus
f
optional reinforcement for young voices
Pa-me-la Hea - man, Vic-to - ria Sy - monds. Be - ne - dic - tus, be - ne - dic - tus
f
Den - nis Ar - scott, San - dra Do-no-van.
f
Mi - chael Col - lins, Ro - bert Cof - fey.
12
f
51
Is he who comes in the name of the Lord
yw'r hwn sy'n dyfod yn enw yr Arglwydd.
Hosanna in the highest,
Hosanna yn y goruchaf.
qui ve - nit in no - mi - ne Do - mi - ni. Ho - san-na in ex-cel - sis,
qui ve - nit in no - mi - ne Do - mi - ni. Ho - san-na in ex-cel - sis,
qui ve - nit in no - mi - ne Do - mi - ni. Ho - san-na in ex-cel - sis,
qui ve - nit in no - mi - ne Do - mi - ni. Ho - san-na in ex-cel - sis,

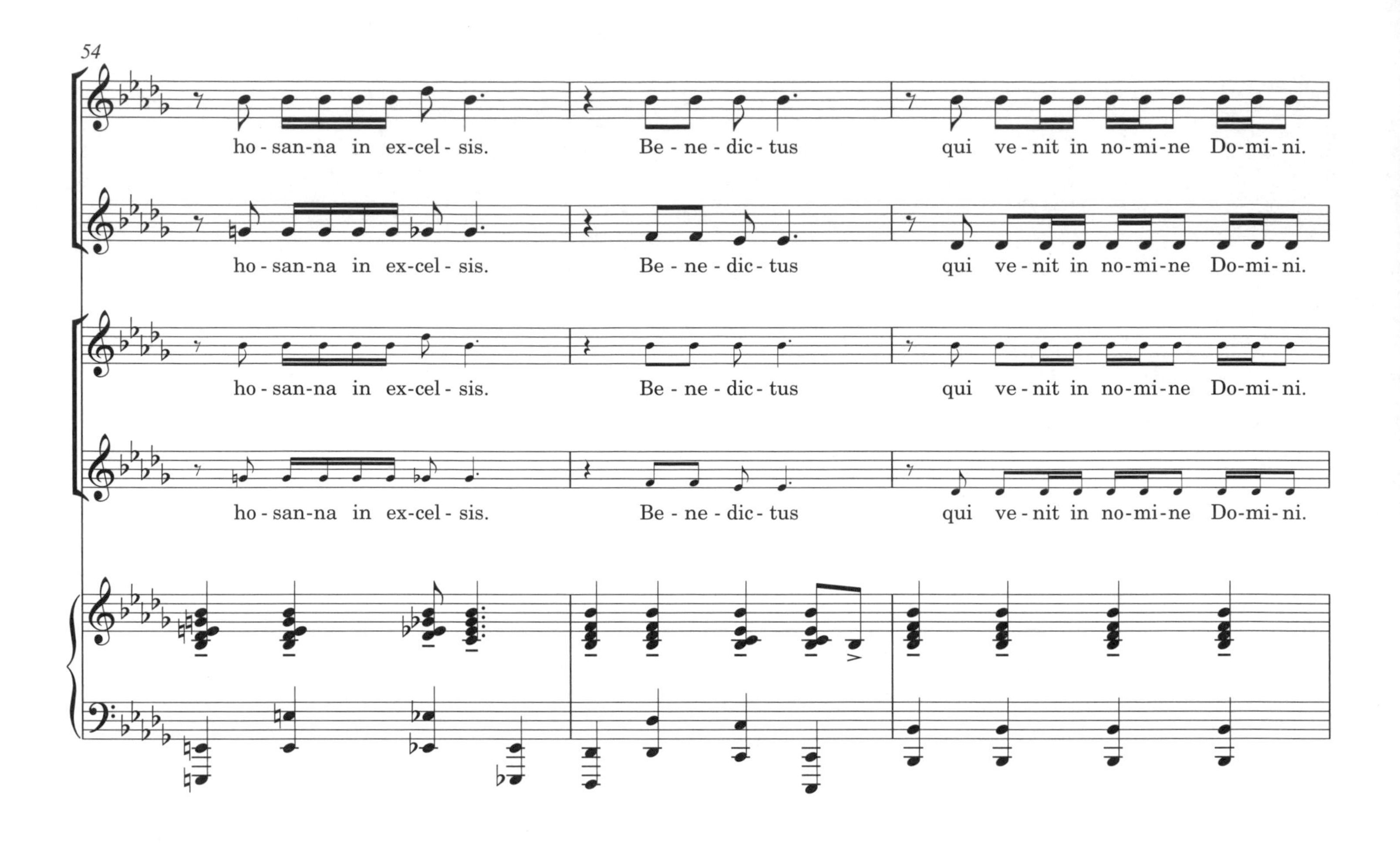
54
ho-san-na in ex-cel-sis.
Be-ne-dic-tus
qui ve-nit in no-mi-ne Do-mi-ni.
ho-san-na in ex-cel-sis.
Be-ne-dic-tus
qui ve-nit in no-mi-ne Do-mi-ni.
ho-san-na in ex-cel-sis.
Be-ne-dic-tus
qui ve-nit in no-mi-ne Do-mi-ni.
ho-san-na in ex-cel-sis.
Be-ne-dic-tus
qui ve-nit in no-mi-ne Do-mi-ni.

57
SOPRANO
mf
An-drew Rees,
Ray-mond John and Pe-ter Col-lins,
ALTO
mf
Des-mond Car-pen-ter, Ed-win Da-vies E-vans, John An-tho-ny King,
TENOR
mf
Jo-seph Wilk-shire, Ro-ger Sum-mers, Da-vid Ga-reth Da-vies, How-ard Da-vid Pros-ser,
BASS
mf
Cath'-rine E-liz-a-beth E-vans, A-vis E-liz-a-beth Sul-li-van,
mf

59
Su - san Crot - ty, Ann-ette Hughes, Sha - ron Le - wis, An - tho - ny Jo - seph
Jen - ni - fer Haines, Jean Wi - ni fred and Mau - reen Ma - ry E - vans, Kay Bowns,
Dwyn - wen Grif - fiths, Bet - ty Ed - wi - na Bart - lett, Lor - raine I - so - bel
Gil - lian and Bri - an Mi - chael Gough, Ran - dolph Tu - dor, Ro - bert Or - ville Jones,
3

61
Wat - kins, Da - vid Wil - liam Wil - liams, Ann Cath'-rine Lee, Lyn - da and Ca - rol
Ca - rol Ann Car - pen - ter, Roy - ston Hod - kin - son, Pat and Tom - my Pro - bert, Gra - ham Wil - liams,
Rich - ards, Kel - vin Da - vid and Mal - colm An - drew, Ne - cia James,
Lyn Hard - ing, Mer - rill Bar - nard, I - an Dou - gall, An - ge - la Wil - liams,

63
An - der - son, San-dra Ley-shon, Ma - ry-lyn and Carl Mi-nett.
Paul Da-vid Ro-berts, Ja - net Jones, Syl - via Rich-ards, Paul Da - vies.
Jill and Vin-cent Par - fitt, Wil - liam Mi-chael and Shei - la Fitz-pat - rick.
Arth-ur O' - Bri - en, Cor-wyn T and Leigh-ton Ker-rie Reakes, Dyf - rig Hayes.

65
f
Be-ne-dic-tus, be-ne-dic-tus qui ve - nit in no-mi - ne Do - mi-ni.
Be-ne-dic-tus, be-ne-dic-tus qui ve - nit in no-mi - ne Do - mi-ni.
Be-ne-dic-tus, be-ne-dic-tus qui ve - nit in no-mi - ne Do - mi-ni.
Be-ne-dic-tus, be-ne-dic-tus qui ve - nit in no-mi - ne Do - mi-ni.

69
Ho - san - na in ex - cel - sis,
ho - san - na in ex - cel - sis.
Ho - san - na in ex - cel - sis,
ho - san - na in ex - cel - sis.
Ho - san - na in ex - cel - sis,
ho - san - na in ex - cel - sis.
Ho - san - na in ex - cel - sis,
ho - san - na in ex - cel - sis.
71
Be - ne - dic - tus,
qui ve - nit in no - mi - ne Do - mi - ni.
Be - ne - dic - tus,
qui ve - nit in no - mi - ne Do - mi - ni.
Be - ne - dic - tus,
qui ve - nit in no - mi - ne Do - mi - ni.
Be - ne - dic - tus,
qui ve - nit in no - mi - ne Do - mi - ni.
73
13
YOUNG VOICES div in 3
Adult victims
1
Rich - ard Jones, Le - wis and Gle - nys Gab - riel Jones, Pa - tri - cia Mar-g'ret E - vans,
2
E - van George and Mar-g'ret Jane Cars - ton, John Mor-gan Ed-wards, Bri - an El - vet Har - ris,
3
13

75
1
Gwy-neth Col-lins,
Gra-ham Ed-ward and Sid-ney Rus-sell,
Y Vces 2
Nan-si Will-iams, Cas-sie Jones,
Tyd-fil Jane Tay-lor,
3
3
77
1
Will-iam Hen-ry Rees,
Fred-'rick Rich-ard Han-sen,
Y Vces 2
Myr-tle I-rene and Will-iam Charles Tho-mas,
Ev'-lyn Ma-ry Jones, Lu-cy May and
3
Mar-ga-ret-ta Bates,
79
1
Su-san-nah Pro-bert,
Mar-jo-rie Chris-tine E-vans.
Y Vces 2
Al-bert Ger-ald Myt-ton, Da-vid Bey-non,
Mar-jo-rie Ann Rees.
3
Mi-chael Da-vies,
Ann Jen-nings.

14
81 SOPRANO cresc
Be - ne-dic - tus, be - ne-dic - tus, be - ne-dic - tus, be - ne-dic - tus.
ALTO cresc
Be - ne-dic - tus, be - ne-dic - tus, be - ne-dic - tus, be - ne-dic - tus.
TENOR cresc
Be - ne-dic - tus, be - ne-dic - tus, be - ne - dic - tus, be - ne-dic - tus.
BASS cresc
Be - ne-dic - tus, be - ne-dic - tus, be - ne - dic - tus, be - ne-dic - tus.
14
cresc

85
As the rain falls so too do the tears.
f
Bu-ried a - live by the Na-tion-al Coal Board. Bw-rw glaw mân ac mae'r da - grau yn dis - gyn.
Boo-roo glou mahn ak my'r dag - rye un dis - kin.
f
Bu-ried a - live by the Na-tion-al Coal Board. Bw-rw glaw mân ac mae'r da - grau yn dis - gyn.
Boo-roo glou mahn ak my'r dag - rye un dis - kin.
f
Bu - ried, bu - ried, bu - ried, bu - ried. Bw - rw, bw - rw, bw - rw, bw - rw.
Boo - roo, boo - roo, boo - roo, boo - roo.
f
Bu - ried, bu - ried, bu - ried, bu - ried. Bw - rw, bw - rw, bw - rw, bw - rw.
Boo - roo, boo - roo, boo - roo, boo - roo.
sim
f

87
Bu-ried a - live, bu-ried a - live. Bw - rw glaw mân ac mae'r da - grau yn dis - gyn.
Boo-roo glou mahn ak my'r dag - rye un dis - kin.
Bu-ried a - live, bu-ried a - live. Bw - rw glaw mân ac mae'r da - grau yn dis - gyn.
Boo-roo glou mahn ak my'r dag - rye un dis - kin.
Bu - ried, bu - ried, bu - ried, bu - ried, bw - rw, bw - rw, bw - rw, bw - rw.
boo - roo, boo - roo, boo - roo, boo - roo.
Bu - ried, bu - ried, bu - ried, bu - ried, bw - rw, bw - rw, bw - rw, bw - rw.
boo - roo, boo - roo, boo - roo, boo - roo.
89
Bu - - - ried, bw - - - rw,
boo - - - roo,
Bu - ried, bw - rw, bu - ried, bw - rw,
boo - roo, boo - roo,
Bu - ried, bw - rw, bu - ried, bw - rw,
boo - roo, boo - roo,
Bu - ried, bw - rw, bu - ried, bw - rw,
boo - roo, boo - roo,

91
bu-ried a - live by the Na-tion-al Coal Board. Bw-rw glaw mân ac mae'r da - grau yn dis - gyn.
Boo-roo glou mahn ak my'r dag - rye un dis - kin.
bu - ried, bw - rw, bw-rw glaw mân ac mae'r da - grau yn dis - gyn.
boo - roo, boo-roo glou mahn ak my'r dag - rye un dis - kin.
bu - ried, bw - rw, bw-rw glaw mân ac mae'r da - grau yn dis - gyn.
boo - roo, boo-roo glou mahn ak my'r dag - rye un dis - kin.
bu - ried, bw - rw, bw-rw glaw mân ac mae'r da - grau yn dis - gyn.
boo - roo, boo-roo glou mahn ak my'r dag - rye un dis - kin.
93
dim
Bu-ried a - live, bu-ried a - live, Bw-rw glaw mân ac mae'r da - grau yn dis - gyn.
Boo-roo glou mahn ak my'r dag - rye un dis - kin.
dim
Bu-ried a - live, bu-ried a - live, Bw-rw glaw mân ac mae'r da - grau yn dis - gyn.
Boo-roo glou mahn ak my'r dag - rye un dis - kin.
dim
Bu-ried a - live, bu-ried a - live, Bw-rw glaw mân ac mae'r da - grau yn dis - gyn.
Boo-roo glou mahn ak my'r dag - rye un dis - kin.
dim
Bu-ried a - live, bu-ried a - live, Bw-rw glaw mân ac mae'r da - grau yn dis - gyn.
Boo-roo glou mahn ak my'r dag - rye un dis - kin.
dim

95
15
BARITONE SOLO mp dim
Bw - rw glaw mân ac mae'r da - grau yn dis - gyn,
Boo-roo glou mahn ak my'r dag - rye un dis - kin,
(dim)
mp
Bu-ried a - live by the Na-tion-al Coal Board.
97
bw - rw, bw - rw, bw - rw, bw - rw.
boo - roo, boo - roo, boo - roo, boo - roo.
Bu-ried a - live by the Na-tion-al Coal Board,
99
rall
pp
bu-ried, bu-ried, bu-ried, bu-ried, bu-ried, bu-ried, bu-ried, bu-ried, bu - - - ried.

4 – Lament for the Valley
Marwnad y Cwm

Agnus Dei

a tempo
YOUNG VOICES
mp
Lamb of God,
Oen Duw,
13
A - gnus De - i, A - gnus De - i,
a tempo
17
A - gnus De - i, A - gnus De - i,
who takes away the sins of the world,
sy'n tynnu ymaith bechodau'r byd:
have mercy on us,
trugarha wrthym,
21
16
S Solo
mp
qui tol - lis pec - ca - ta mun - di, mi - se - re - re no - bis,
Bar Solo
mp
qui tol - lis pec - ca - ta mun - di, mi - se - re - re no - bis,
Y Vces
mp
qui tol - lis pec - ca - ta mun - di, mi - se - re - re no - bis,
T B
mp in the style of a monastic chant
qui tol - lis pec - ca - ta mun - di, mi - se - re - re no - bis,
16

grant us peace.
dyro inni dy dangnefedd.
25
17
qui tol-lis pec-ca-ta mun-di, do - na no-bis pa - - cem,
qui tol-lis pec-ca-ta mun-di, do - na no-bis pa - - cem,
qui tol-lis pec-ca-ta mun-di, do - na no-bis pa - - cem,
qui tol-lis pec-ca-ta mun-di, do - na no-bis pa - - cem,
17

30
5

33
3
poco rall

18
a tempo
37
SOPRANO SOLO
mp
qui tol - lis pec - ca - ta mun - di, do - na no - bis pa - - cem.
BARITONE SOLO
mp
qui tol - lis pec - ca - ta mun - di, do - na no - bis pa - - cem.
YOUNG VOICES
mp
qui tol - lis pec - ca - ta mun - di, do - na no - bis pa - - cem.
S/A
mp
qui tol - lis pec - ca - ta mun - di, do - na no - bis pa - - cem.
T/B
mp
18
a tempo
41
19
19
mf

45
8
8
loco

49
20
SOPRANO SOLO
mp
A -
BARITONE SOLO
mp
sim
A - gnus, A - gnus, A - gnus, A -
YOUNG VOICES
mp
A - gnus, A - gnus, A - gnus,
SOPRANO/ALTO
unis
mp
A - gnus, A - gnus, A - gnus,
TENOR/BASS
unis
mp
20
p

53
sim
poco rall
gnus, A - gnus, A - - gnus De - i.
gnus, A - gnus, A - - gnus De - i.
A - gnus, A - gnus, A - gnus De - i.
A - gnus, A - gnus, A - gnus De - i.
poco rall

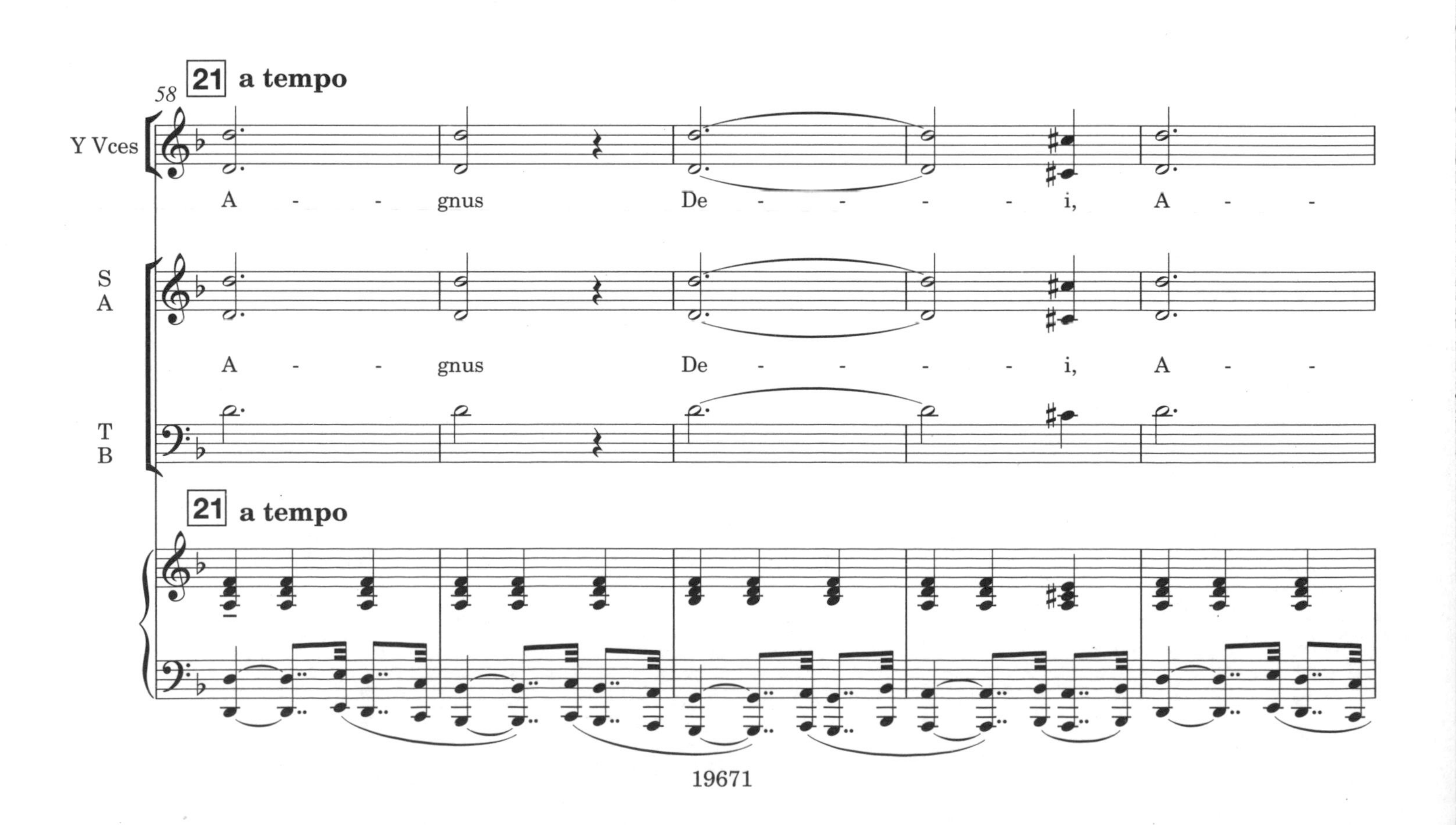
21 a tempo
58
Y Vces
A - - gnus De - - - - - i, A - -
S
A
A - - gnus De - - - - - i, A - -
T
B
21 a tempo

63
-gnus
De
-
-
-
-
i,
-gnus
De
-
-
-
-
i,
69
SOPRANO SOLO
mp
rall
De - i.
BARITONE SOLO
mp
De - i.
p
A - gnus De - i,
De - i,
De - i.
unis
De - i.
rall

5 – Lacrimosa Lullaby

Lacrimosa 'Maban Glân

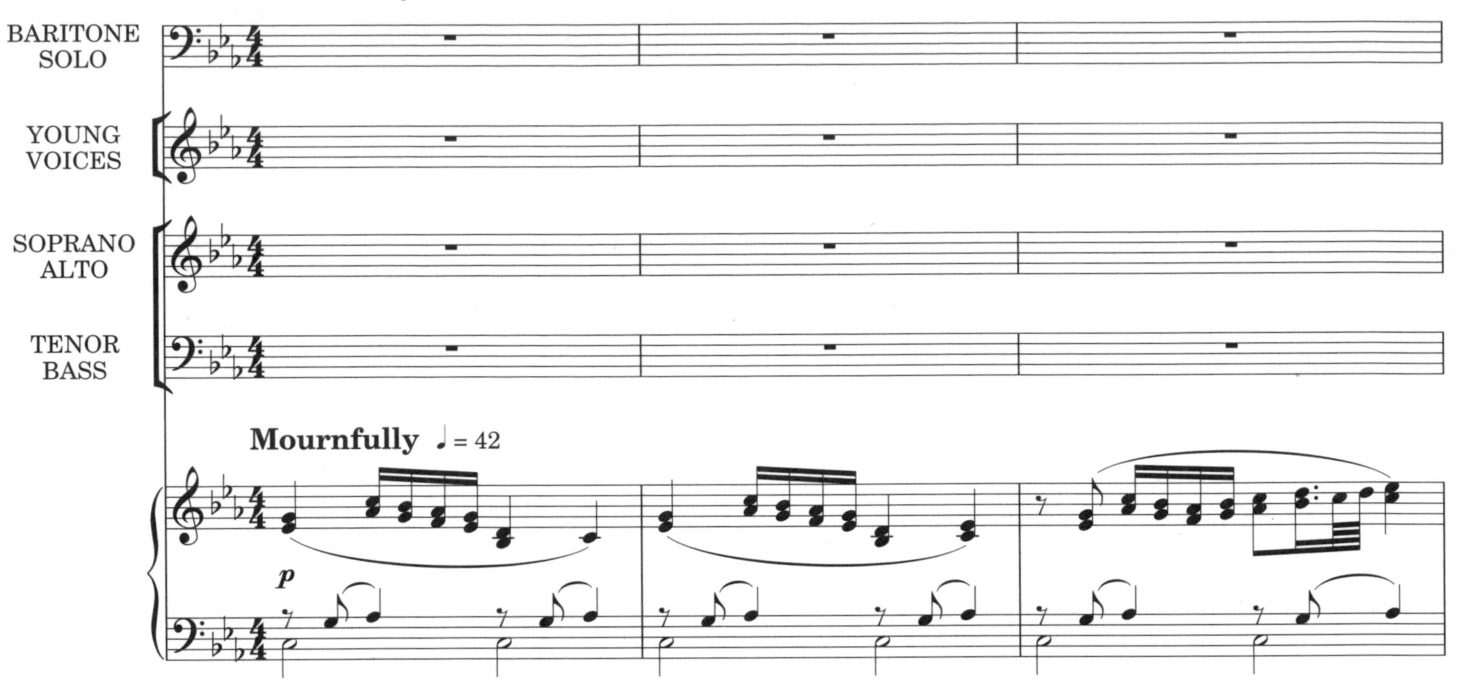

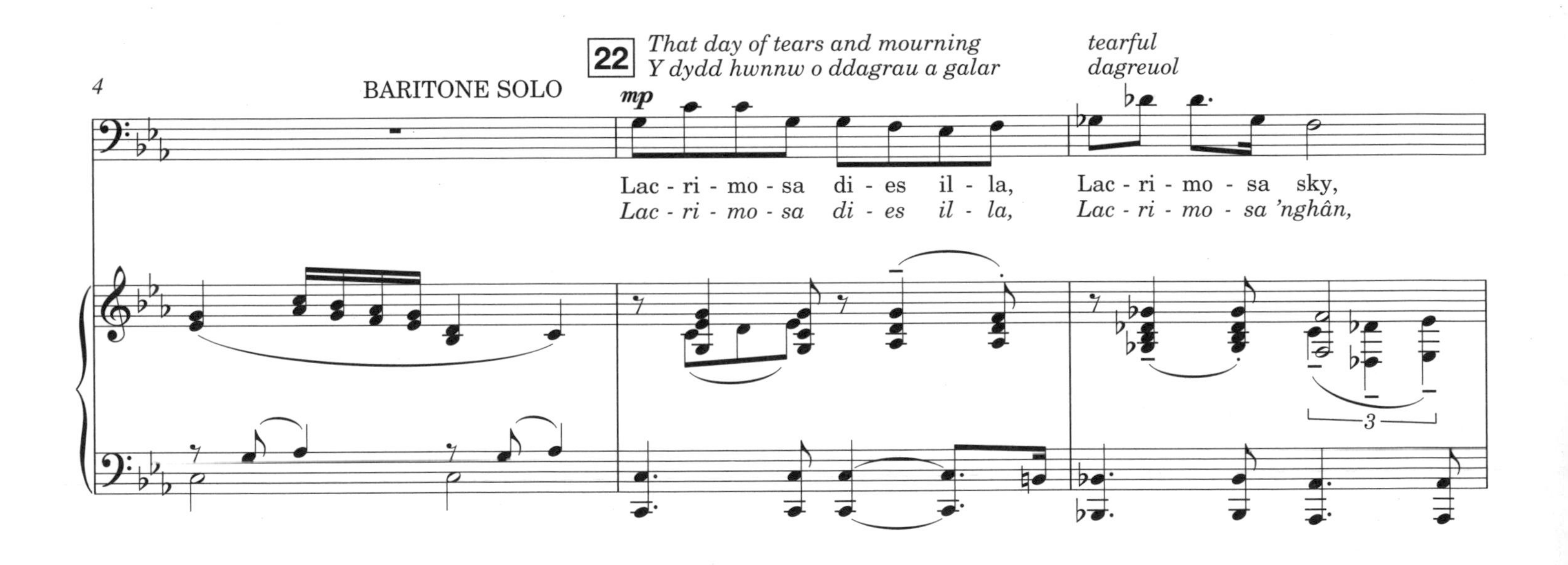

10
Lac - ri - mo - sa sigh, Lac - ri - mo - sa rain-drops qui - ver, Lac - ri - mo - sa lull - a -
Lac - ri - mo - sa'r cwm, Lac - ri - mo - sa dag - rau'n cry - nu, Lac - ri - mo - sa 'nga - lar
3
13 23
Bar Solo
- by.
trwm.
That day of tears and mourning, when from the ashes shall arise all humanity to be judged,
Y dydd hwnnw o ddagrau a galar, pan gyfyd o'r llwch yr holl fyd i farnedigaeth,
mp
Y Vces
Lac - ri - mo - sa di - es il - la, Qua re - sur - get ex fa - vil - la Ju - di - can - dus ho - mo re - us:
T
Lac - ri - mo - sa, lac - ri - mo - sa, la - cri - mo - sa,
B
Lac - ri - mo - sa, lac - ri -
23
spare us by your mercy, Lord.
gwared ni drwy dy drugaredd, O Arglwydd.
Gentle Lord Jesus,
Iesu'r Arglwydd Tirion,
grant them eternal rest.
rhodded iddynt dragwyddol hedd.
16
Pi - e Je - su Do - mi - ne, do - na e - is re - qui - em.
Hu - ic er - go par - ce De - us. do - na e - is re - qui - em.
lac - ri - mo - sa, lac - ri - mo - sa, lac - ri - mo - sa, lac - ri - mo - sa, lac - ri - mo - sa, lac - ri - mo - sa.
- mo - sa, lac - ri - mo - sa.

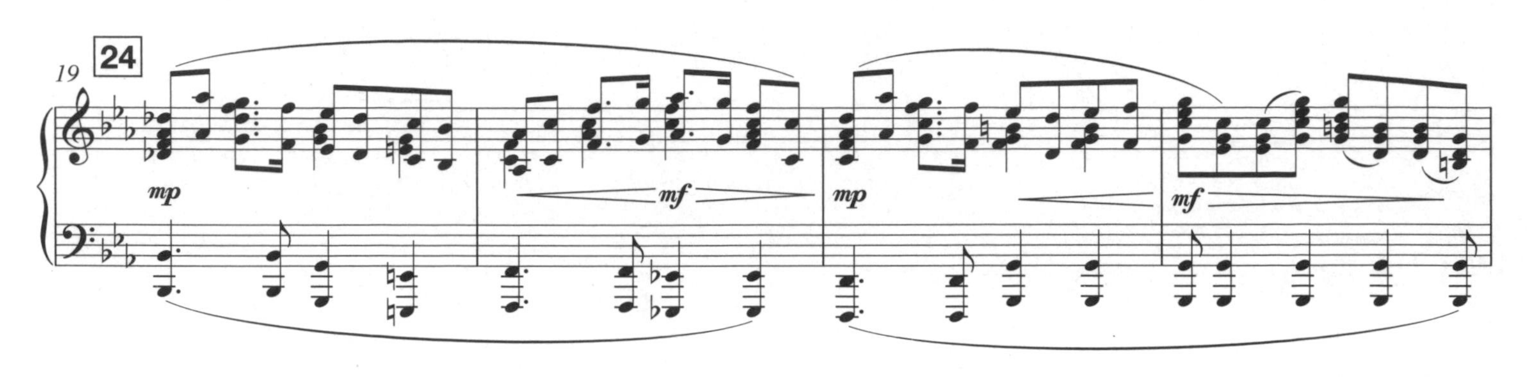
24
19
mp
mf
mp
mf

25
BARITONE SOLO
23
mp
Lac - ri - mo - sa,
lac - ri - mo - sa.
YOUNG VOICES
mp
Lac - ri - mo - sa_ lull - a - by,
Lac - ri - mo - sa_'ma - ban glân,
SOPRANO
mp
Lac - ri - mo - sa_ lull - a - by,
Lac - ri - mo - sa_'ma - ban glân,
ALTO
mp
Lac - ri - mo - sa_ lull - a - by,
Lac - ri - mo - sa_'ma - ban glân,
TENOR
mp
Lac-ri-mo - sa, lac-ri-mo-sa, lac-ri-mo - sa, lac-ri-mo-sa, lac-ri-mo - sa, lac-ri-mo-sa,
BASS
mp
Lac - - ri - - mo - - sa, lac - - ri -
25
mp

26
26
Lac - ri - mo - sa sil - ver ar - rows, Lac - ri - mo - sa cry,
Lac - ri - mo - sa'n sae-thau ar - ian, Lac - ri - mo - sa'n gri,
lac - ri - mo - sa lull - a - by.
lac - ri - mo - sa 'ma - ban glân.
lac - ri - mo - sa lull - a - by.
lac - ri - mo - sa 'ma - ban glân.
lac - ri - mo - sa lull - a - by.
lac - ri - mo - sa 'ma - ban glân.
lac-ri-mo - sa, lac-ri - mo - sa.
-mo - - sa.
26

29
Lac - ri - mo - sa hurt my heart - beat, Lac - ri - mo - sa lull - a - by, Lac - ri - mo - sa si - lent fea - thers,
Lac - ri - mo - sa'n gur - iad ca - lon, Lac - ri - mo - sa 'ngh - lon i, Lac - ri - mo - sa'r blu - en ddis - taw,

32
Lac - ri - mo - sa fly,
Lac - ri - mo - sa dos,
Lac - ri - mo - sa__ hush my ba - by,
Lac - ri - mo - sa__ hysh fy mhlen - tyn,
Lac - ri-mo - sa lull - a - by.
Lac - ri-mo - sa cys - ga'r nos.

27
SOPRANO
ALTO
TENOR
BASS
35
mf
Lac - ri - mo - sa di - es - il - la, Qua re - sur - get ex fa - vil - la Ju - di - can - dus ho - mo - re - us:
mp

38
YOUNG VOICES
28
mp
Pi - e Je - su Do - mi-ne,
mp
Hu - ic er - go par - ce De - us.
Pi - e Je - su Do - mi-ne,
Hu - ic er - go par - ce De - us.
Pi - e Je - su Do - mi-ne,
Hu - ic er - go par - ce De - us.
Lac-ri-mo - sa, lac-ri-mo - sa
Hu - ic er - go par - ce De - us.
Lac - ri - mo - sa
28
41 BARITONE SOLO
do - na e - is re - qui - em.
do - na e - is re - qui - em.
do - na e - is re - qui - em.
lac - ri - mo - sa, lac - ri - mo - sa.
lac - ri - mo - sa.

43
BARITONE SOLO
Lac - ri - mo - sa lull - a - by,
Lac - ri - mo - sa 'ma - ban glân,
YOUNG VOICES
Lac - ri - mo - sa lull - a - by.
Lac - ri - mo - sa 'ma - ban glân.
Lac - ri - mo - sa.
46
lac - ri - mo - sa lull - a - by,
lac - ri - mo - sa 'ma - ban glân,
dim
mm
mm
dim
49
rall
mp
lac - ri - mo - sa lull - a - by.
lac - ri - mo - sa 'ma - ban glân.
mm
(dim)
p

6 – Did I hear a bird?

11
mp
(But I don't think so, but I don't think so.)
-go. (But I don't think so, but I don't think so.)
tr
17
29
Did I hear the flut-ter of wings, f - f-flut-ter of wings, Like the
5
21
Un - rav - el - rav - el - rav - el - ling, un -
sound of a-pron strings Un - rav - el - rav - el - rav - el - ling, un -

25
-rav-el-rav-el-rav-el-rav-el-rav-el - ling?
-rav-el-rav-el-rav-el-rav-el-rav-el - ling?
30
30
BARITONE SOLO mf
That keeps on fall - ing, fall - ing, fall - ing,
YOUNG VOICES
mf
What have I heard? Just a lit - tle, lit - tle, lit - tle bird
30
mp
35
from an emp - ty thun - der - cloud, That keeps on fall - ing, fall - ing, fall - ing, fall - ing, fall - ing,
mf
That keeps on fall - ing, fall - ing, fall - ing, fall - ing, fall - ing,
8

38
31
SOPRANO SOLO
mf
ah ah ah ah ah ah ah ah ah ah ah ah ah ah
Sound-ing of loss – a loss so loud.
Sound-ing of loss – a loss so loud.
SA unis
p Tonight, little children
bed, little children
He - no, he - no, Hen blant bach, Gwe - ly, gwe - ly,
Heh - no, heh - no, Hehn blant bach, Gweh - lee, gweh - lee,
(8)
31
Ped
sim
42
ah ah ah ah ah ah ah ah ah ah ah ah ah ah ah
halfpenny, little children
Hen blant bach, Di - me, di - me, di - me, Hen blant bach,
Hehn blant bach, Di - meh, di - meh, di - meh, Hehn blant bach,
45
32
mp
ah ah ah ah ah ah ah ah ah ah ah ah ah ah ah ah ah ah ah ah ah
halfpenny, little children
Di - me, di - me, di - me, Hen blant bach.
Di - meh, di - meh, di - meh, Hehn blant bach.
32
8
p
6
6

50
33
tr
ah
ah
BARITONE SOLO mp
Hear a bird?
YOUNG VOICES mp
Can you hear a bird? Just a
p
55
Just a word? Can you hear a song? 'Twas long a - go, But I don't think so, but I
word? Can you hear a song? 'Twas long a - go, But I don't think so, but I
60
doh-doh-doh-doh doh-doh-doh-doh-don't think so.
doh-doh-doh-doh doh-doh-doh-doh-don't think so.

63
34
Can you hear the flut-ter of wings, f - f-flut-ter of wings, Like the
67
SOPRANO SOLO
mp
A-pron strings hear a beat - ing, beat-ing wing, hear a
sound of a-pron strings? beat - ing, beat-ing wing, hear a
YOUNG VOICES
Hear a beat-ing, beat-ing, beat-ing wing, hear a
71
be-be-be-be-be-be-be-be beat-ing wing.
be-be-be-be-be-be-be-be beat-ing wing.
be-be-be-be-be-be-be-be beat-ing wing?

75
BARITONE SOLO
35
mf
Beat - ing my heart, just a lit - tle, lit - tle, lit - tle
YOUNG VOICES
mf
Beat - ing my heart, just a lit - tle, lit - tle, lit - tle
35
5
mp
79
SOPRANO SOLO
mf
sim
ah ah ah sim
bird That keeps on call - ing, call - ing, call - ing, Call - ing soft - ly from the
bird That keeps on call - ing, call - ing, call - ing, Call - ing soft - ly from the
82
crowd, That keeps on call - ing, call - ing, call-ing, call-ing, call - ing,
crowd, That keeps on call - ing, call - ing, call-ing, call-ing, call - ing,
8

84
36
ah
Call-ing for light, A light so loud.
Call-ing for light, A light so loud.
Tacet to end if recorders are used
Tomorow, little children
mp
Fo - ry, fo - ry,
Vo - ree, vo - ree,
Hen blant bach,
Hehn blant bach,
mp
(8)
36
p

87
ah
ah ah ah ah ah
sim
ah ah ah ah
bed, little children
Gwe - ly, gwe - ly,
Gweh - lee, gweh - lee,
Hen blant bach,
Hehn blant bach,
halfpenny, little children
Di - me, di - me, di - me,
Di-meh, di-meh, di - meh,

90
ah
ah ah ah ah
ah ah ah ah ah ah ah ah ah ah ah ah
ah
halfpenny, little children
Hen blant bach,
Hehn blant bach,
Di - me, di - me, di - me,
Di-meh,di-meh,di - meh,
Hen blant bach.
Hehn blant bach.
93
ah ah sim
98
rall
103
ah

7 – Satin Feathers

Aderyn Du

16
3
clo - ser,__ Bring the sun and make it gold - en, Bring the dai - sies to my gar - den.
cu - ddio,__ Dod â'r blo - dau nôl i dy - fu, Dod â'r heul - wen aur i we - nu?
21
SOPRANO SOLO
38
mp
Bring the mu - sic to my val - ley, Bring it
A - de - ryn du,__ a ga'i dy ffein - dio Yn y
BARITONE SOLO
mp
Bring the mu - sic to my val - ley, Bring it
A - de - ryn du, a ga'i dy ffein - dio Yn y
38
mp
26
5
back a - gain and hur - ry,__ Bring the joy and bring the laugh - ter, Bring them
cwm yn ca - nu e - to?__ Tyrd â'r miw - sig, tyrd â'r chwa - re, Tyrd â'r
Optional
back a - gain and hur - ry, Bring the joy__ and bring the laugh - ter,__ Bring them
cwm yn ca - nu e - to? Tyrd â'r miw - sig, tyrd â'r chwa - re,__ Tyrd â'r

30
back to stay for - ev - er.
plant yn ddio - gel ad - re.
back to stay for - ev - er.
plant yn ddio - gel ad - re.
34
p rubato
a piacere
39 a tempo
One, two, three things I can't i - ma-gine That my
Un, dau, tri pheth sy'n a-nodd i - mi, Cyf-ri'r
8
tr
39 a tempo
ppp
7
p
39
bird with wings of sat - in Takes the night, the moon, the shad - ow, And brings my
sêr pan fo hi'n rhe - wi, pwy - so sof - rens aur yr ei - thin, A de - all
p
Takes the night, the moon, the shad - ow, And brings my
Pwy - so sof - rens aur yr ei - thin, A de - all

43
child - ren home to - mor - row, brings our child - - ren home
i ble'r aeth y chwer-thin, de - all i ble'r aeth
child - ren home to - mor - row, brings our child - - ren home
i ble'r aeth y chwer-thin, de - all i ble'r aeth
48
40
to - mor - row.
y chwer-thin.
to - mor - row.
y chwer-thin.
YOUNG VOICES
mf
Bring the mu - sic to my val - ley, Bring it
A - de - ryn du, a ga'i dy ffein - dio Yn y
SOPRANO
mf
Bring the mu - sic to my val - ley, Bring it
A - de - ryn du, a ga'i dy ffein - dio Yn y
ALTO
mf
Bring the mu - sic to my val - ley, Bring it
A - de - ryn du, a ga'i dy ffein - dio Yn y
TENOR
mf
Bring the mu - sic to my val - ley, Bring it
A - de - ryn du, a ga'i dy ffein - dio Yn y
BASS
mf
Bring the mu - sic to my val - ley, Bring it
A - de - ryn du, a ga'i dy ffein - dio Yn y
40
mf

52
back a - gain and hur - ry, Bring the joy and bring the
cwm yn ca - nu e - to? Tyrd â'r miw - sig, tyrd â'r
55
laugh - ter, Bring them back to stay for - ev - er.
chwa - re, Tyrd â'r plant yn ddio - gel ad - re.
dim poco a poco a fine

59
SOPRANO SOLO
p
For - ev - er.
Nôl a - dre.
BARITONE SOLO
p
For - ev - er.
Nôl a - dre.
For - ev - er.
Nôl a - dre.
pp
For - ev - er.
Nôl a - dre.
pp
For - ev - er.
Nôl a - dre.
pp
For - ev - er.
Nôl a - dre.
pp
For - ev - er.
Nôl a - dre.

65
rall
1
ppp

8 – And-a-half
Blwyddyn-a-mis

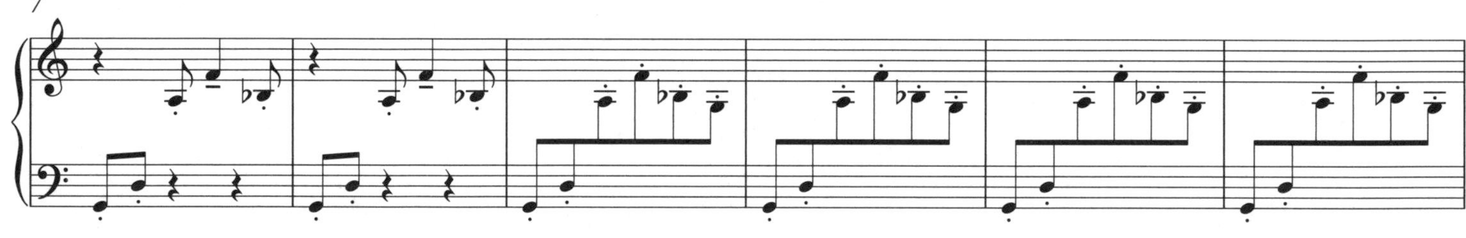

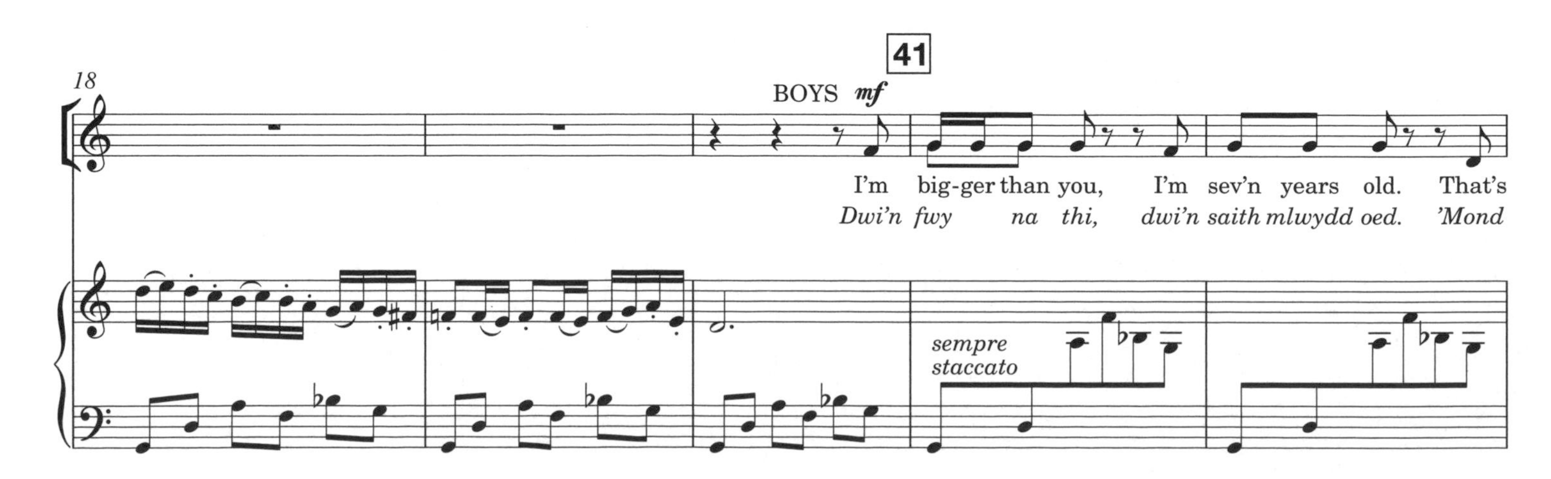

23
no - thing – I'm sev'n and a half!
hyn - ny? Dwi'n saith mlwydd a mis!
I'm strong-er than you, I'm eight years old. That's
Dwi'n gry - fach na thi, dwi'n wyth mlwydd oed. 'Mond
27
GIRLS mf
no - thing – I'm eight and a half!
hyn - ny? Dwi'n wyth mlwydd a mis!
I'm pret - ti - er than you – I'm nine years old. That's
Dwi'n bert - ach, lot, na thi, dwi'n naw mlwydd oed. 'Mond
31
no- thing – I'm nine and a half!
hyn - ny? Dwi'n naw mlwydd a mis!
35
ALL
42
I'm cle - ver - er than you – I'm ten and a quar - ter. That's
Dwi'n ddoeth - ach, lot, na thi, dwi'n ddeg, bron, a han - ner. 'Mond
sempre staccato

39
BOYS
no- thing – I'm ten and a half! If you're so big, tell Bil - ly he's slow! I
hyn - ny? Wel dwi'n un deg un! A thi mor fawr, dwed wrth Jac: ti'n slo'! All -
43
can't to - day, I've got a bad toe. If you're so strong, go on lift this stone! I
- a'i ddim nawr, na'i 'neud ryw-bryd 'to. A thi mor gryf, co - da'r gar - reg hon! All -
47
ALL
can't to - day, I've got a bad... bone. He can't to - day, he's got a bad... bone.
- a'i ddim nawr, mewn crys new-ydd sbon. All e ddim nawr, mewn crys new-ydd sbon.
51
BOYS
43
GIRLS
If you're so pret - ty give John-ny a kiss. But
A thi mor bryd-ferth rho gu - san i Ben. Ond mae

55
BOYS
ALL
John-ny is ug - ly. For shame I'll tell Miss! If you're so cle - ver, what's three
Ben - i'n rhy sa - lw. Dwi'n dweud wrth Miss Gwen! A thi mor gly - far, beth yw
58
hun-dred mil-lion di - vi-ded by nine o-ver two? That's ea - sy pea - sy le - mon
tair mil-iwn pum cant we - di rhan - nu gy-da thri? Mae hynn-y'n haws na chaws na
62
squee - zy... but I'm not tell - ing you!
phaw - si... ond so fi'n gweud'tho ti!
66

44 With a sense of nostalgia
70
SOPRANO
mf più legato
And some - where be - tween the years - and - a - half, When the
A rhyw - le'n y bwlch rhwng blwy - ddyn a mis, A'r haul
ALTO
mf più legato
And some - where be - tween the years - and - a - half, When the
A rhyw - le'n y bwlch rhwng blwy - ddyn a mis, A'r haul
TENOR
mf più legato
And some - where be - tween the years - and - a - half, When the
A rhyw - le'n y bwlch rhwng blwy - ddyn a mis, A'r haul
BASS
mf più legato
And some - where be - tween the years - and - a - half, When the
A rhyw - le'n y bwlch rhwng blwy - ddyn a mis, A'r haul
44 With a sense of nostalgia
mp
Ped.
sim
75
sky would skip and the sun would laugh, When the yard was the sea and the
yn rhoi'i aur heb ho - li am bris, Ar yr iard roedd y môr, a'r hen
sky would skip and the sun would laugh, When the yard was the sea and the
yn rhoi'i aur heb ho - li am bris, Ar yr iard roedd y môr, a'r hen
sky would skip and the sun would laugh, When the yard was the sea and the
yn rhoi'i aur heb ho - li am bris, Ar yr iard roedd y môr, a'r hen
sky would skip and the sun would laugh, When the yard was the sea and the
yn rhoi'i aur heb ho - li am bris, Ar yr iard roedd y môr, a'r hen

81
wall was the land, When the whole wide world could fit in a hand,
wal fach pen draw Yd-oedd ffin y byd mawr a phawb law yn llaw,
wall was the land, When the whole wide world could fit in a hand,
wal fach pen draw Yd-oedd ffin y byd mawr a phawb law yn llaw,
wall was the land, When the whole wide world could fit in a hand,
wal fach pen draw Yd-oedd ffin y byd mawr a phawb law yn llaw,
wall was the land, When the whole wide world could fit in a hand,
wal fach pen draw Yd-oedd ffin y byd mawr a phawb law yn llaw,

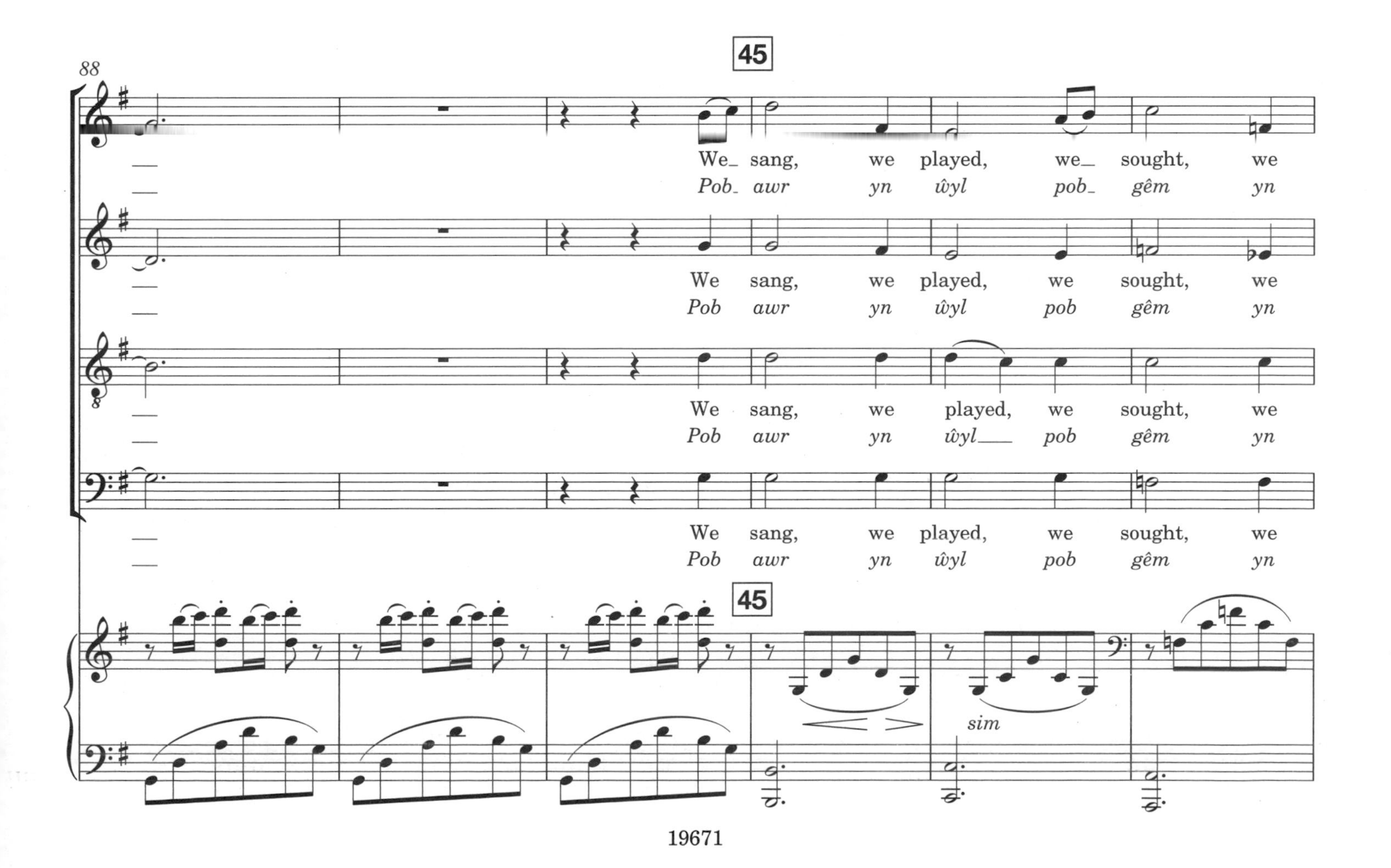
88
45
We sang, we played, we sought, we
Pob awr yn ŵyl pob gêm yn
We sang, we played, we sought, we
Pob awr yn ŵyl pob gêm yn
We sang, we played, we sought, we
Pob awr yn ŵyl pob gêm yn
We sang, we played, we sought, we
Pob awr yn ŵyl pob gêm yn
45
sim

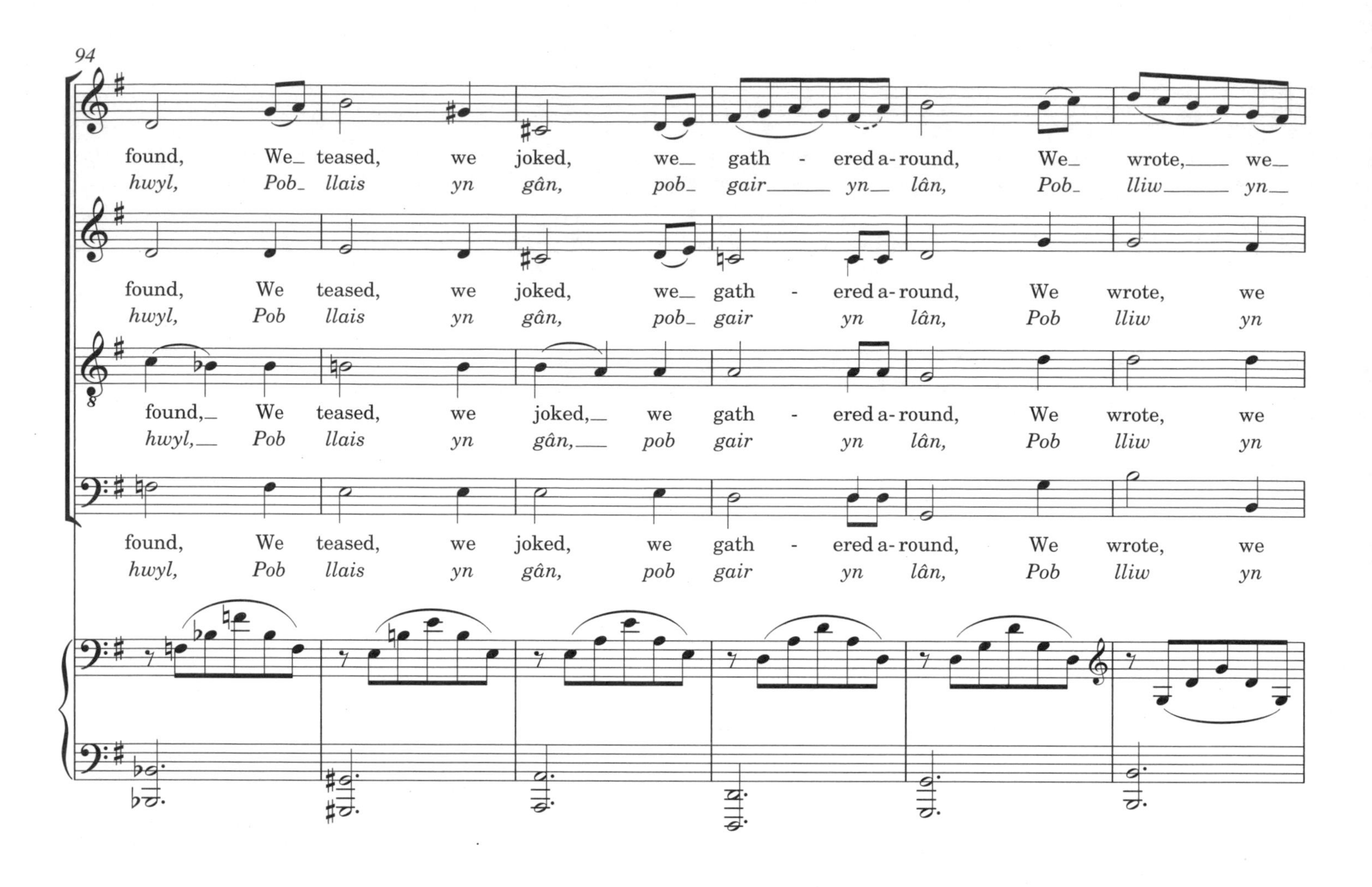
94
found, We_ teased, we joked, we_ gath - ered a-round, We_ wrote,___ we_
hwyl, Pob_ llais yn gân, pob_ gair___ yn_ lân, Pob_ lliw___ yn_
found, We teased, we joked, we_ gath - ered a-round, We wrote, we
hwyl, Pob llais yn gân, pob_ gair yn lân, Pob lliw yn
found,_ We teased, we joked,_ we gath - ered a-round, We wrote, we
hwyl,_ Pob llais yn gân,___ pob gair yn lân, Pob lliw yn
found, We teased, we joked, we gath - ered a-round, We wrote, we
hwyl, Pob llais yn gân, pob gair yn lân, Pob lliw yn

100
read, we_ built___ we_ drew, Be - fore the years - and - a-half all___
llun, pob_ gwg___ yn_ wên, Cyn hed - fan y mi - is-oedd oll___ yn_
read, we built we drew, Be - fore the years - and - a-half all
llun, pob gwg yn wên, Cyn hed - fan y mi - si-oedd oll yn
read,_ we built we drew,_ Be - fore the years - and - a-half all
llun,_ pob gwg yn wên,_ Cyn hed - fan y mi - is-oedd oll yn
read, we built we drew, Be - fore the years - and - a-half all
llun, pob gwg yn wên, Cyn hed - fan y mi - is-oedd oll yn

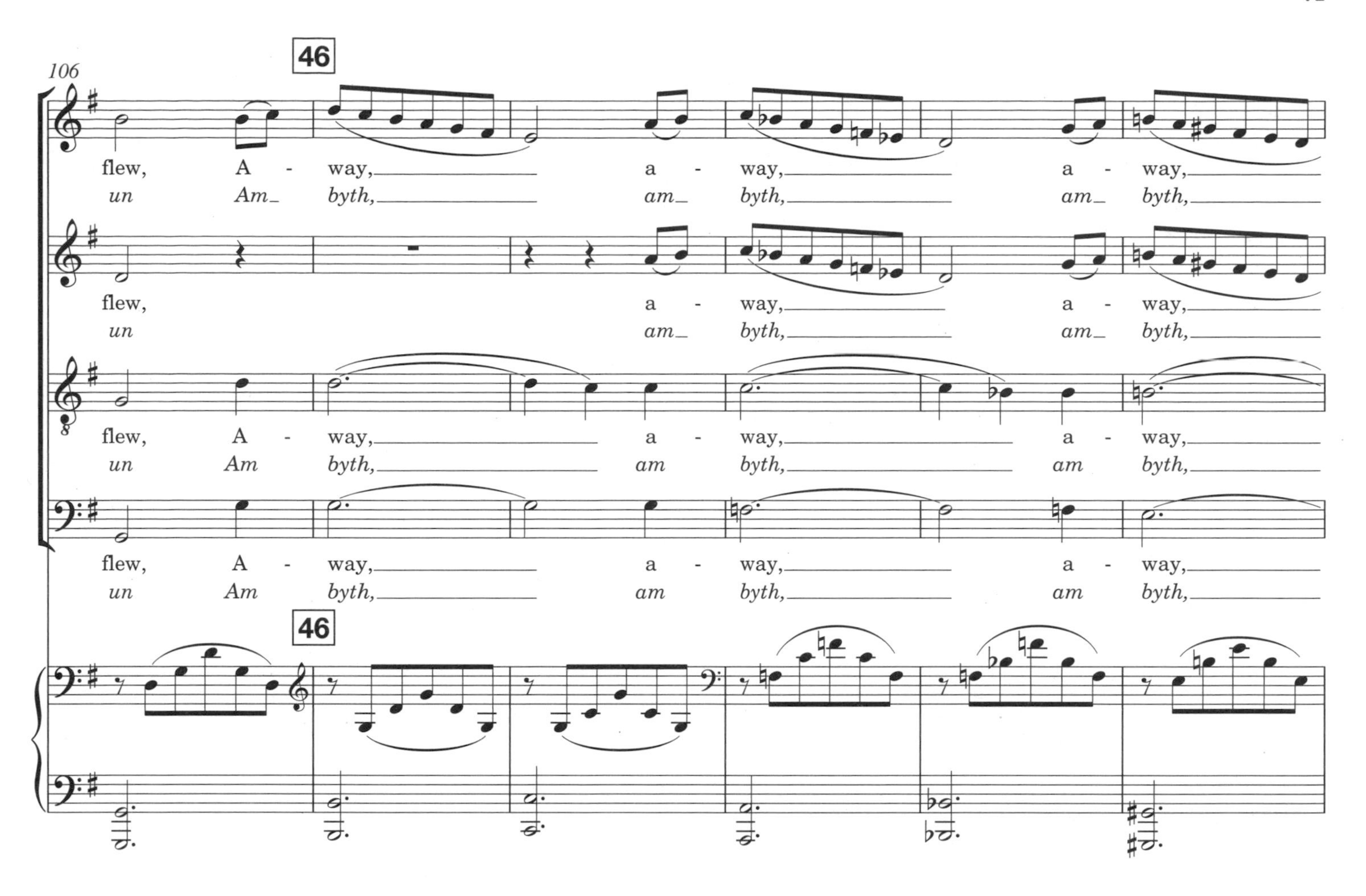
106
46
flew, A - way, a - way, a - way,
un Am_ byth, am_ byth, am_ byth,
flew, a - way, a - way,
un am_ byth, am_ byth,
flew, A - way, a - way, a - way,
un Am byth, am byth, am byth,
flew, A - way, a - way, a - way,
un Am byth, am byth, am byth,
46

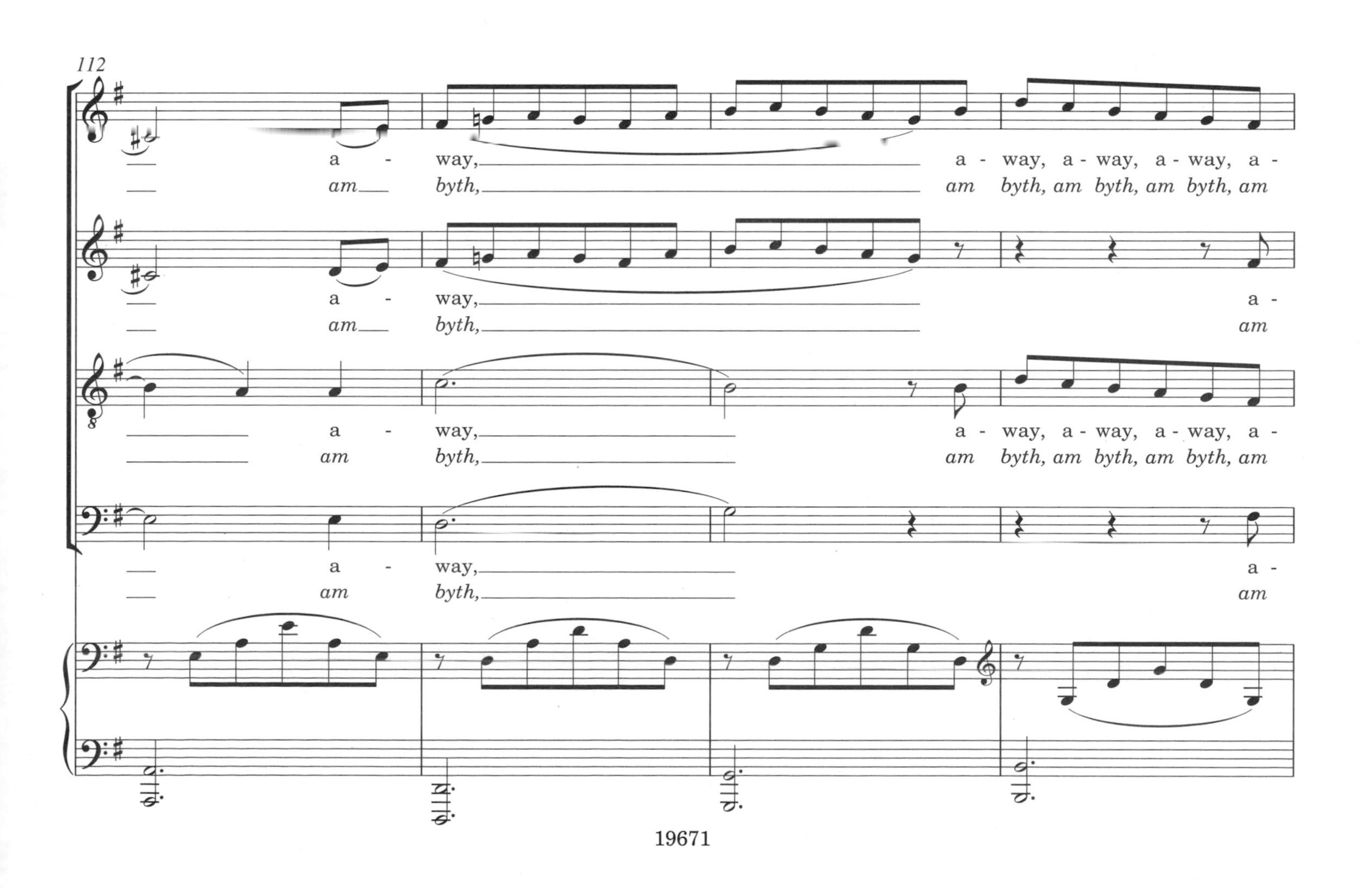
112
a - way, a - way, a - way, a - way, a -
am_ byth, am byth, am byth, am byth, am
a - way, a -
am_ byth, am
a - way, a - way, a - way, a - way, a -
am byth, am byth, am byth, am byth, am
a - way, a -
am byth, am

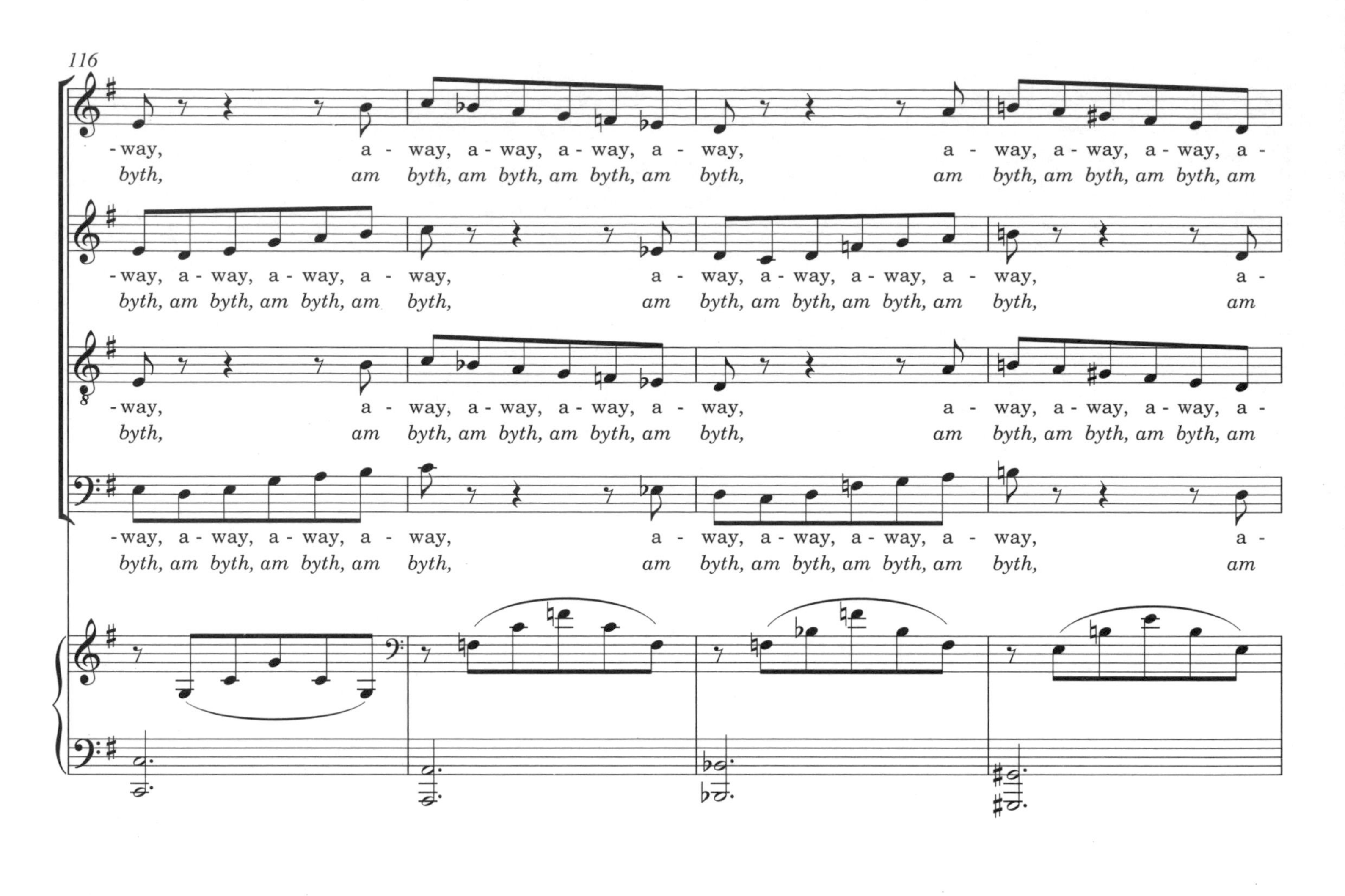
116
-way, a - way, a - way, a - way, a - way, a - way, a - way, a - way, a -
byth, am byth, am byth, am byth, am byth, am byth, am byth, am byth, am
-way, a - way, a - way, a - way, a - way, a - way, a - way, a - way, a - way, a -
byth, am byth, am byth, am byth, am byth, am byth, am byth, am byth, am byth, am
-way, a - way, a - way, a - way, a - way, a - way, a - way, a - way, a -
byth, am byth, am byth, am byth, am byth, am byth, am byth, am byth, am
-way, a - way, a - way, a - way, a - way, a - way, a - way, a - way, a - way, a -
byth, am byth, am byth, am byth, am byth, am byth, am byth, am byth, am byth, am

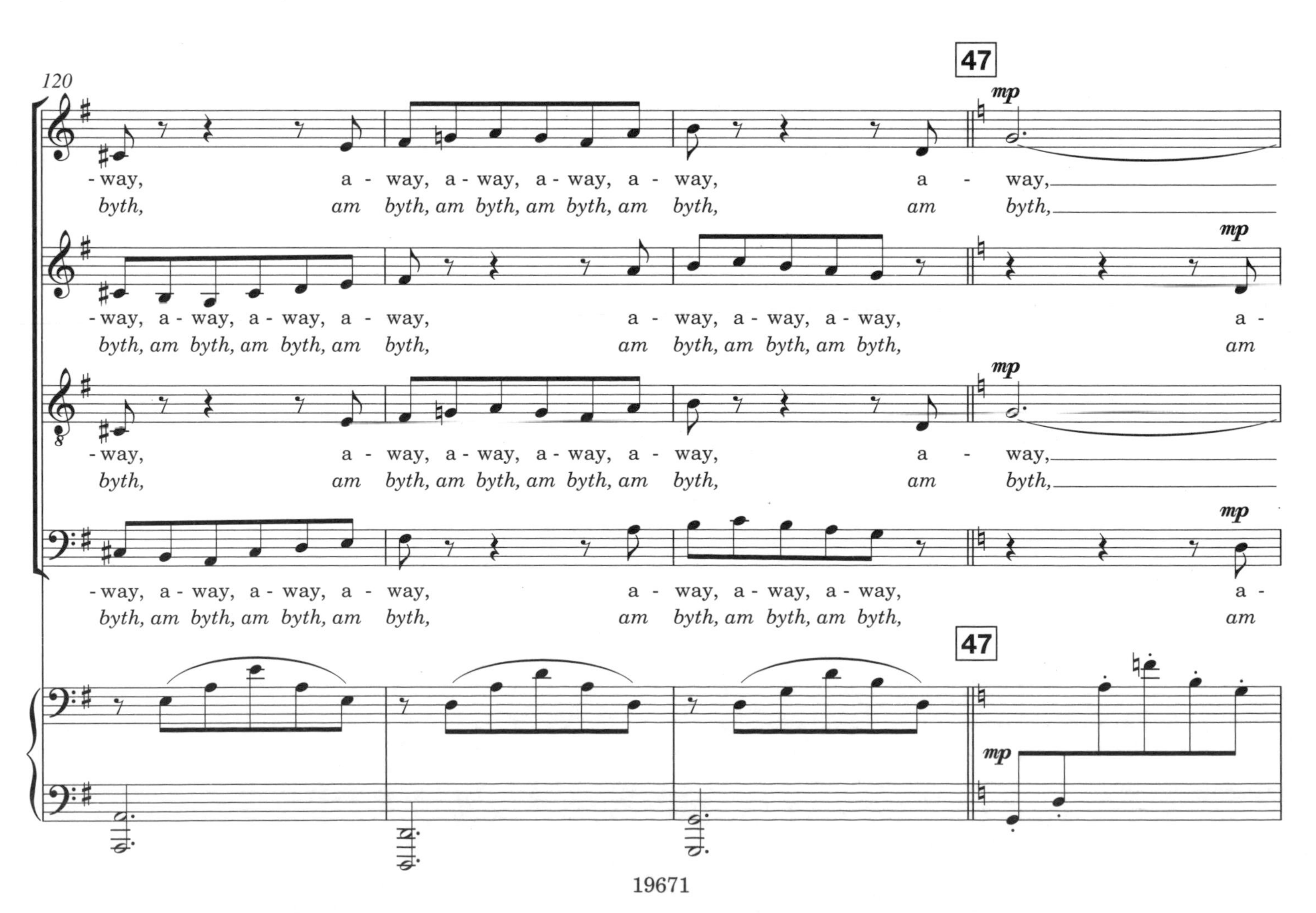
120
47
mp
-way, a - way, a - way, a - way, a - way, a - way,
byth, am byth, am byth, am byth, am byth, am byth,
mp
-way, a - way, a - way, a - way, a - way, a - way, a - way, a - way, a -
byth, am byth, am byth, am byth, am byth, am byth, am byth, am byth, am
mp
-way, a - way, a - way, a - way, a - way, a - way,
byth, am byth, am byth, am byth, am byth, am byth,
mp
-way, a - way, a - way, a - way, a - way, a - way, a - way, a - way, a -
byth, am byth, am byth, am byth, am byth, am byth, am byth, am byth, am
47
mp

124
p
— a - way, a - way, a-
— am byth, am byth, am
-way, a - way, a - way, a - way, a - way, a - way, a - way, a - way, a - way,
byth, am byth, am byth, am byth, am byth, am byth, am byth, am byth, am byth,
-way, a - way, a - way, a - way, a - way, a - way, a - way, a - way, a - way,
byth, am byth, am byth, am byth, am byth, am byth, am byth, am byth, am byth,
dim
p dim
sempre staccato

129
pp
-way, a - way, a - way,
byth, am byth, am byth,
a - way, a - way, a - way, a - way, a - way, a - way, a-
am byth, am byth, am byth, am byth, am byth, am byth, am
pp dim

134
ppp
a - way.
am byth.
-way, a - way, a - way,
byth, am byth, am byth,
a - way, a - way, a - way, a - way, a - way, a - way, a -
am byth, am byth, am byth, am byth, am byth, am byth, am
ppp dim
138
-way, a - way, a - way, a - way.
byth, am byth, am byth, am byth.
dim al niente
143
(Hp, Percussion)
3

9 – And once upon a time
Unwaith amser maith yn ôl

14/40
mf
-fore the end of each be - gin - ing,
chyn y diw-edd i bob dech - rau,
Once up - on a time,
Am-ser maith yn ôl,
once up - on a time,
am-ser maith yn ôl,
SOPRANO
mp
ah
ALTO
TENOR
BASS
48
20/46
S
A
T
B
Once up - on,
Am - ser maith,
once up - on,
am - ser maith,
once up - on a
am - ser maith yn
time
ôl
that was
d'am-ser
yours
di

25/51
S Solo
yours
di
Bar Solo
yours
di
S
and mine.
a mi.
A
and mine.
a mi.
T
and mine.
a mi.
B
and mine.
a mi.
57
49
mp seamless; stagger breathing
And once up - on a time, When time was to - geth - er, When the worlds were near - er
Ac am - ser maith yn ôl, Dydd - iau dau yn dynn - ach, Pob dim yn ag - os - ach,
mp seamless; stagger breathing
And once up - on a time, When time was to - geth - er, When the worlds were near - er
Ac am - ser maith yn ôl, Dydd - iau dau yn dynn - ach, Pob dim yn ag - os - ach,
Baritones sing if tenor 'light'.
mp seamless; stagger breathing
And once u - pon a time, When time was to - geth - er, When the worlds were near - er
Ac am - ser maith yn ôl, Dydd - iau dau yn dynn - ach, Pob dim yn ag - os - ach,
49
p

61
And the skies were clear - er, Once up - on a time, When time was for - ev - er and to - mor - row nev - er,
Aer uwch - ben yn las - ach, Am - ser maith yn ôl, Dydd - iau dau'n fyth byth - oedd ac y - fo - ry'n oes - oedd,
And the skies were clear - er, Once up - on a time, When time was for - ev - er and to - mor - row nev - er,
Aer uwch - ben yn las - ach, Am - ser maith yn ôl, Dydd - iau dau'n fyth byth - oedd ac y - fo - ry'n oes - oedd,
And the skies were clear - er, Once up - on a time, When time was for - ev - er and to - mor - row nev - er,
Aer uwch - ben yn las - ach, Am - ser maith yn ôl, Dydd - iau dau'n fyth byth - oedd ac y - fo - ry'n oes - oedd,
65
YOUNG VOICES
1st time: tacet
Descant 2nd time only
50
mp seamless; stagger breathing
Once u - pon a time, once u - pon a time,
Am - ser maith yn ôl, am - ser maith yn ôl,
In that once up - on a time that was yours and mine, Once up - on a time, When time was to - geth - er,
Yn ein ham - ser maith yn ôl, d'am - ser di a mi, Am - ser maith yn ôl, Dydd - iau dau yn dynn - ach,
mp
yours and mine, Once up - on a time, When time was to - geth - er,
di a mi, Am - ser maith yn ôl, Dydd - iau dau yn dynn - ach,
In that once up - on a time that was yours and mine, Once up - on a time, When time was to - geth - er,
Yn ein ham - ser maith yn ôl, d'am - ser di a mi, Am - ser maith yn ôl, Dydd - iau dau yn dynn - ach,
In that once up - on a time that was yours and mine, Once up - on a time, When time was to - geth - er,
Yn ein ham - ser maith yn ôl, d'am - ser di a mi, Am - ser maith yn ôl, Dydd - iau dau yn dynn - ach,
50

70/80
once u - pon a time, once u - pon a time, once u - pon a time, once u - pon a time,
am - ser maith yn ôl, am - ser maith yn ôl, am - ser maith yn ôl, am - ser maith yn ôl,
When the worlds were near - er And the skies were clear - er, Once up - on a time, When time was for - ev - er
Pob dim yn ag - os - ach, Aer uwch - ben yn las - ach, Am - ser maith yn ôl, Dydd - iau dau'n fyth byth oedd
74/84
once u - pon a time, once u - pon a time, yours and mine,
am - ser maith yn ôl, am - ser maith yn ôl, di a mi,
and to - mor - row nev - er, In that once up - on a time that was yours and mine,
ac y - fo - ry'n oes - oedd, Yn ein ham - ser maith yn ôl, d'am - ser di a mi,

88
SOPRANO SOLO
rall
yours and mine.
di a mi.
BARITONE SOLO
yours and mine.
di a mi.
yours and mine.
di a mi.
Yours and mine.
Dim ond ni.
Yours and mine.
Dim ond ni.
Yours and mine.
Dim ond ni.
Yours and mine.
Dim ond ni.
rall

10 – When the shadow dies

12
That has no dawn, say, And
shall we mourn by the shal-low moon No day, Shall we stay?
15
still, Shall we grieve by the shal - low grave Of a flown - a - way life like a fal - len
Of a flown - a - way life like a fal - len
17
leaf, And if so,
leaf, how?

20
23
51
p
And when win-ter blows, Might we rest by the emp-ty tree? Should I?
Shall we try? No-bo-dy
51
pp
26
knows.
But if to be a-live is to be-long
Then we

29
Keep
This
must
Still
song.
3
52 Positively
32
optional to bar 40
poco f
S Solo
Sing it un-til the end of the night,
Sing it, sing it for our child-ren loved light.
Ca-nwn
Ca-nwn, ca-nwn
Bar Solo
Sing it un-til the end of the night,
Sing it, sing it for our child-ren loved light. Sing
Ca-nwn
Ca-nwn, ca-nwn
Ca -
S
Sing it un-til the end of the night,
Sing it, sing it for our child-ren loved light.
Ca-nwn
Ca-nwn, ca-nwn
A
Sing it un-til the end of the night,
Sing it, sing it for our child-ren loved light.
Ca - nwn
Ca - nwn, ca-nwn
T
Sing it un-til the end of the night,
Sing it, sing it for our child-ren loved light. Sing
Ca-nwn
Ca-nwn, ca-nwn
Ca -
B
Sing it un-til the end of the night,
Sing it, sing it for our child-ren loved light. Sing
Ca-nwn
Ca-nwn, ca-nwn
Ca -
52 Positively
poco f

36
Sing it un-til the end of the night, Sing it, sing it, for our
Ca-nwn Ca-nwn, ca-nwn
it un-til the end of the night, Sing it, sing it, for our
- nwn Ca-nwn, ca-nwn
YOUNG VOICES
poco f
Sing. Sing. Sing. Sing. Sing.
Sing it un-til the end of the night, Sing it, sing it, for our
Ca-nwn Ca-nwn, ca-nwn
Sing it un-til the end of the night, Sing it, sing it, for our
Ca-nwn Ca - nwn, ca-nwn
it, sing it, un-til the end of the night, Sing it, sing it, for our
- nwn, ca - nwn Ca-nwn, ca-nwn
it, sing it, un-til the end of the night, Sing it, sing it, for our
- nwn ca - nwn Ca-nwn, ca-nwn

rall
39
child-ren loved_ light, our child-ren loved_ light, my child___ loved light.
child-ren loved_ light, our child-ren loved_ light, my child___ loved light.
Light.___ Light.___
child-ren loved_ light, our child-ren loved_ light.
child-ren loved light, our child-ren loved light.
child-ren loved light, our child-ren loved light.
child-ren loved light, our child-ren loved light.
rall

11 – Lux æterna

54
16
SOPRANO SOLO
poco mf
cum sanc - tis, cum sanc-tis
BARITONE SOLO
poco mf
cum sanc - tis, cum sanc-tis
sanc - tis
'Light' in various languages.
Latin
SOPRANO
mp
Lux.
English
p
Light.
Italian
Lu - ce.
ALTO
mp
Lux.
p
Light.
Lu - ce.
54
mp
20
tu - is, in æ - ter - num, qui - a pi-us es.
tu - is, in æ - ter - num, qui - a pi-us es.
German
Licht.
Swedish
Li - jus.
Welsh
Go - leu - ni.
Goh - lie - nee.
Licht.
Li - jus.
Go - leu - ni.
Goh - lie - nee.

55
25
Latin
English
Italian
German
Lux. Light. Lu - ce. Licht.
Lux. Light. Lu - ce. Licht.
YOUNG VOICES
Lux. Light. Lu - ce. Licht.
Eternal rest grant them, O Lord,
Dyro iddynt orffwys tragwyddol, O Arglwydd,
Re - qui-em æ - ter - nam do - na e - is, Do - mi-ne,
Re - qui-em æ - ter - nam do - na e - is, Do - mi-ne,
TENOR
Re - qui-em æ - ter - nam do - na e - is, Do - mi-ne,
BASS
Re - qui-em æ - ter - nam do - na e - is, Do - mi-ne,
55

29
Swedish
Welsh
Li - jus. Go - leu - ni.
Li - jus. Go - leu - ni.
Latin
Li - jus. Lux.
and let perpetual light shine upon them, for you are merciful.
a llewyrched goleuni tragwyddol arnynt, oherwydd trugarog wyt ti.
et lux per - pe - tu - a lu - ce - at e - is, qui - a pi - us
et lux per - pe - tu - a lu - ce - at e - is, qui - a pi - us
et lux per - pe - tu - a lu - ce - at e - is, qui - a pi - us
et lux per - pe - tu - a lu - ce - at e - is, qui - a pi - us

56
𝅗𝅥 = 60
Y Vces
S
A
T
B
mp
If
Pe
es.
es.
es.
es.
p
6
I were a beau-ti-ful twink-ling star I'd shine on the dark-est night, I'd
bawn i yn se-ren fach lo-yw lân Yn gwe-nu ar fron y nos, Mi
seek where the drear-i-est path-ways are And light them with all my might. Though
fyn-nwn ole-uo'r holl gong-lau du A'r ffordd sydd yn mynd i'r rhos. Er

45
div in 3
div in 2
sun and moon I can - not be To make the whole world bright, I'd
nad wyf i Na haul na lloer I'r cre - ad mawr i gyd, Gall
ALTO p
To make the whole world bright, I'd
I'r cre - ad mawr i gyd, Gall
TENOR p
I'd
Gall
8
49
find some lit - tle cheer - less spot And shine with all my might.
plen - tyn by - chan la - wen - hau Un cor - nel bach o'r byd.

★Optional: some Tenors may double this

75
58
Star of light,
Star of fire,
Light,
SOPRANO
ALTO
TENOR
BASS
mp
Sêr y Gol - eu - ni, Se - ren dân, Gol - eu - ni,
Sair uh goll - ay★ - nee, Sair - enn dahn, Goll - ay - nee,
81
Star of song.
mf
Se - ren gân.
Sair - enn gahn.
Sêr y Gol - eu - ni, Se - ren
Sair uh goll - ay - nee, Sair - enn

★'ay' as in 'Amy'

59
YOUNG VOICES
Lux æ - ter - na
dân, Gol - eu - ni, Se - ren gân.
dahn, Goll - ay - nee, Sair - enn gahn.
dân, Gol - eu - ni, Se - ren gân.
dahn, Goll - ay - nee, Sair - enn gahn.
dân, Gol - eu - ni, Se - ren gân.
dahn, Goll - ay - nee, Sair - enn gahn.
dân, Gol - eu - ni, Se - ren gân.
dahn, Goll - ay - nee, Sair - enn gahn.
59
SOPRANO SOLO
cum sanc - tis
BARITONE SOLO
cum sanc - tis
lu - ce - at e - is, Do - mi - ne:

★Pronunciation to rhyme with the corresponding words in Soprano and Alto.

110
mp
li - jus, li - jus, lux, lux, lu - ce, licht, licht, lu - ce, lux.
li - jus, li - jus, lux, lux, lu - ce, licht, licht, lu - ce, lux.
lee, lee, lee, lee, lu, lu, lu, lu, loo, loo, li, li, li, li, loo, loo, lu, lu, lu, lu,
lee, lee, lee, lee, lu, lu, lu, lu, loo, loo, li, li, li, li, loo, loo, lu, lu, lu, lu,

Young Voices, S & A to divide equally
(with regard to sound, not numerically).
61
YOUNG VOICES
115
mp
poco mf
Go - leu - ni, lu - ce, lu - ce, lu - ce, lu - ce,
S
Go - leu - ni, lu - ce, lu - ce, lu - ce, lu - ce,
A
Go - leu - ni, lu - ce, lu - ce, lu - ce, lu - ce,
T
go, go, go, go, lu, lu, lu, lu, lu, lu, lu, lu, lu, lu, lu, lu,
B
go, go, go, go, lu, lu, lu, lu, lu, lu, lu, lu, lu, lu, lu, lu,
61

Readjust part allocation to ensure moving crotchet line is heard.

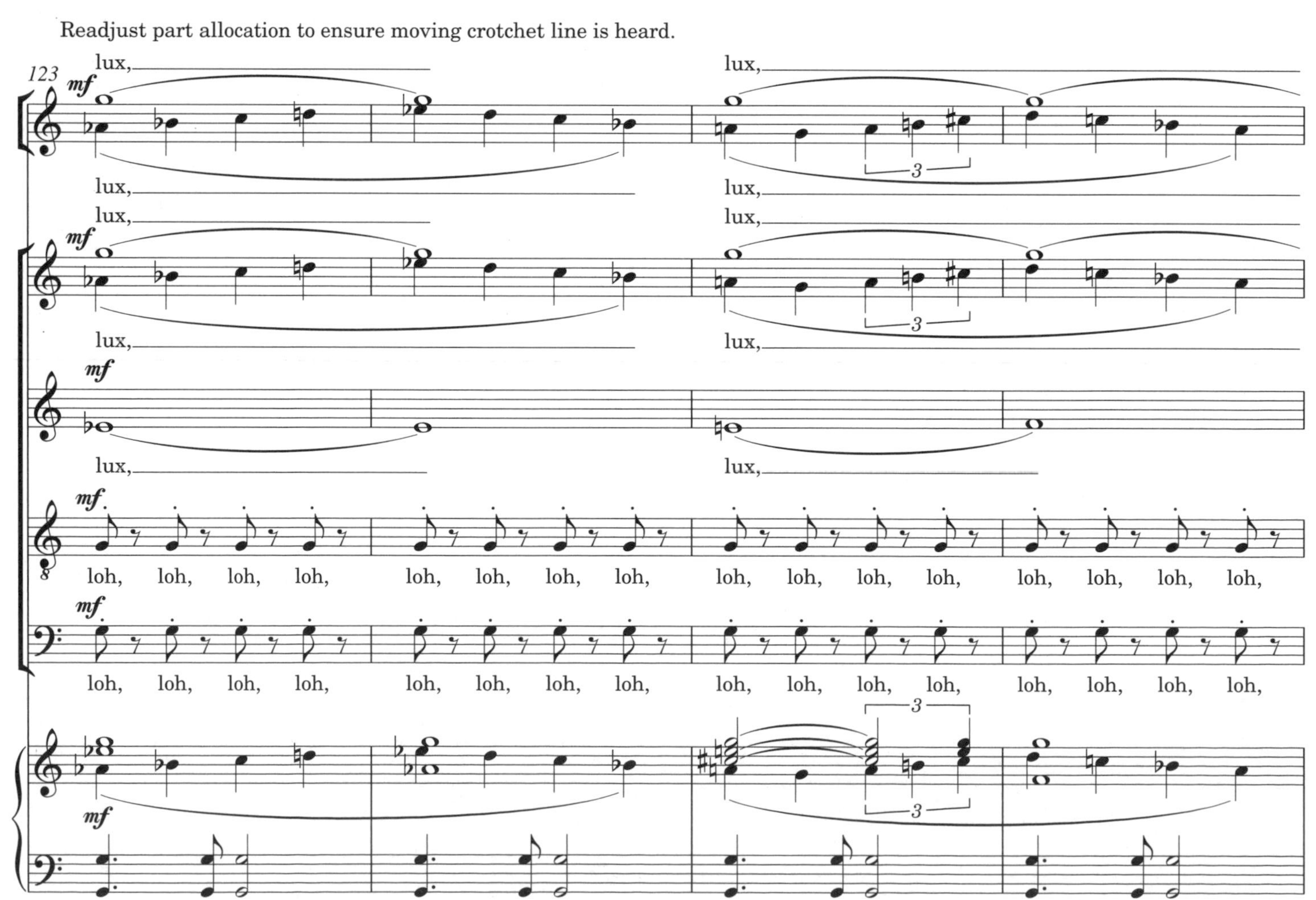

127
lux,
lux,
lux,
lux,
lux,
lux,
loh, loh, loh, loh, loh, loh, loh, loh, loh, loh, loh, loh, loh, loh, loh, loh,
loh, loh, loh, loh, loh, loh, loh, loh, loh, loh, loh, loh, loh, loh, loh, loh,
131
lux,
lux,
lux
lux
lux,
lux,
lux,
lux,
lux,
lux,
loh, loh, loh, loh, loh, loh, loh, loh, loh, loh, loh, loh, loh, loh, loh, loh,
loh, loh, loh, loh, loh, loh, loh, loh, loh, loh, loh, loh, loh, loh, loh, loh,

135
lux.
62
lux.
lux.
lux.
lux.
loh, loh, loh, loh, loh, loh, loh, loh, loh, loh, loh, loh, loh, loh, loh, loh,
loh, loh, loh, loh, loh, loh, loh, loh, loh, loh, loh, loh, loh, loh, loh, loh,
62
pp
Ped
140
144
molto rall
SOPRANO SOLO
pp lunga
a piacere
light.
glân.
YOUNG VOICES
spoken or whispered
light.
glân.